MW00440822

OUTSMARTING
CRAZY
TOWN

A BUSINESS NOVEL ABOUT HOW DERAILED
PROFESSIONALS CAN GET BACK ON TRACK

BRENDA ABDILLA

INDIE BOOKS
INTERNATIONAL®

ISBN: 978-1-952233-16-6
Library of Congress Control Number: 2020913900

Designed by Joni McPherson, mcphersongraphics.com

INDIE BOOKS INTERNATIONAL®
2424 VISTA WAY, SUITE 316
OCEANSIDE, CA 92054

www.indiebooksintl.com

CONTENTS

For my remarkable, resilient clients. Thank you for allowing me to do work that feeds my soul.

PREFACE

{ The Urban Dictionary defines Crazytown as:
*Living in a state of insanity or being around
the crazy/insane of the universe.* }

ARE YOU LIVING IN CRAZYTOWN?

You might be in Crazytown when you finally land your coveted dream job at a Fortune 100 company, but your entire director team aligns to sabotage your every effort and initiative—even going as far as giving you misinformation for reports you provide to the CEO. You quickly realize why you are the fourth VP in two years.

You might be in Crazytown when the charismatic CEO of the company, who is the most inspirational person you have ever worked for, is fired by the new private equity firm. The new CEO, who behaves more like a CFO, has no interest in innovation, product development, or customer satisfaction initiatives—all things in your domain. You go from being completely engaged in your work to a constant state of incredulous frustration.

Crazytown is what you feel after being promoted to senior management and then almost immediately denied "a seat at the table." You are left out of key meetings, important calls, and decisions that impact your team, and you have no idea why. Your peers are also confounded. Any mention of this is summarily dismissed by your supervisor.

Crazytown is working for a newly promoted boss who listens to your phone calls through the thin walls separating your offices, insists on reviewing and editing every communication you send out to the team, and scrutinizes every dollar you spend from your department budget.

Crazytown is when work turns into a headshaking, logic-defying, maddening place for you. Crazytown can be a situation, a state of being, a culture, or just your own private hell—at work.

It may surprise you to hear that most Crazytown workplaces are not created out of evil or malintent—we are not talking about working at Enron. On the contrary, at the core of what has gone awry is usually a good intention. The company is trying to save money, or increase profits, or choose a new product path, or expand their market—all good intentions. It is just that the decisions or changes that come from good intentions may suddenly stop working for you. Crazytown can be that you suddenly work for misguided, inexperienced, even incompetent leaders and are surrounded by an otherwise ideal environment. That still makes it Crazytown for you. Sometimes, Crazytown is finding yourself in a culture of people who are clearly not your people.

Many would suggest that the people who find themselves in Crazytown simply leave and find new jobs. But the entire work landscape is constantly shifting, so switching companies is not always the answer. You could be trading one form of Crazytown for another. Plus, you have made sacrifices to get where you are, and the reputational costs that could be associated with leaving your current post are not to be discounted. In short: *it's complicated.* Wouldn't it be much smarter if there was a way to fortify yourself against the impact of the craziness and *then* decide if you will stay or go?

Crazytown can exist in publicly traded companies, start-ups, nonprofits, government agencies, B-corporations, and every known industry.

Accepting that Crazytown exists both inside and outside of your current organization will result in better decisions about your career trajectory. We all make better decisions when the rationale is based in reality—and the reality is that Crazytown is here to stay. Perhaps you have already left your Crazytown, or were pushed out and are seeking another post. By fortifying yourself against Crazytown, you will gain some perspective on the past, and also make a better cultural and career choice in the future.

MEET MIKE

Get ready to meet Mike Rogers. Mike is a great guy who has a wife and young family in Spokane. He is the senior manager of IT for a small software company that has recently been purchased, and as a result, Mike's life is about to change dramatically.

Some alarming stuff happens at work that throws Mike into a bit of tailspin. All this change happens at a time when Mike is already questioning his choices and his future. He turned forty last year and is wondering about his career, what is meaningful to him, and why this unsettled feeling is growing inside.

But on another level, Mike feels he has no reason to complain or change jobs. He is well compensated and has great benefits. His wife just went back to work after staying home with their girls for seven years. Things are feeling normal at home again. He wonders if maybe he should just suck it up and deal with the changes at work. But Mike is burned out, not sleeping, and starting to dread going to work. He feels trapped.

Lucky for Mike, he finds a mentor who agrees to help him navigate this critical time in his career. His mentor can relate completely to his predicament and takes Mike through some useful processes to clarify his thinking and his career direction. Mike's mentor teaches him that he needs to work in four major "buckets," and that doing so will pay off for the rest of his career by helping him navigate, or outsmart, nearly any kind of Crazytown that comes his way.

FOUR KEYS TO OUTSMARTING CRAZYTOWN

1. **Learn to deal with stress like a boss.** Making career decisions in a triggered state is a bad idea. Burnout is real, and Mike learns how to deal with his career baggage, manage his stress levels in new and important ways, and see where the gaps are in his life. This provides him a level of clarity he has never experienced before.

2. **Figure out your career superpower.** Popular wisdom would have Mike discovering his passion and monetizing it. But nothing could be more confusing for someone at a major crossroads. Instead, Mike learns what superpower skills separate him from others and how detailing the life he really wants can make a huge impact on his direction.

3. **Find your blind spots.** Anyone witnessing unusual or acting-out behavior at work can point a finger and blame. But we all have bad habits or thought processes that block our ability to reach our ultimate level of success. Mike discovers something about his leadership that changes everything.

4. **Develop and leverage your network.** Many professionals who have been working hard and getting results look up one day to realize they have not been developing their network, let alone leveraging it. Mike learns how to develop his network in a way that aligns with his personality and already-busy life so he will never feel trapped again.

This book is a business novel. It is written in story form so that you can derive what you need from the content and apply it to your own life and career.

Enjoy!

Brenda Abdilla

CHAPTER 1

SLEEPLESS IN SPOKANE

Mike Rogers couldn't sleep.

He kept replaying the events over and over again in his mind. A much larger company, MorTech, had recently acquired Mike's employer of fourteen years, Bonzo, where Mike served as the chief technology officer.

Things at work were pretty quiet for the first six months after the acquisition, and nothing really changed. But then, the rug got pulled out from under Mike when his boss, Albert, was fired. Mike thought he and Albert were the victims of undeserved misfortune.

Albert was the chief operating officer (COO) and had been with Bonzo for twenty-five years. Albert mentored Mike and taught him everything he knew about leadership. When Mike first got promoted to CTO, he knew his job like the back of his hand but had no idea how to lead.

Albert took extra time to coach Mike on how to run his team meetings, how to hire and recruit top professionals, how to deal with difficult employees, and how to get his team of independent, sometimes socially awkward IT experts to work together as a cohesive team. Thanks to Albert, Mike had a reputation in the industry for his ability to lead and retain a team.

Mike was shocked that after more than two decades of service, Albert was summarily released. No party. No congratulations. No closure. Just a one-line email from the new CEO.

Mike had a nasty feeling in the pit in his stomach, and it was waking him up every night. Would Mike be the next to walk the plank?

Naturally, after the MorTech merger, Mike was a little worried. But his friends and colleagues in the software industry put his mind at ease. Most of them had not only survived but thrived in the era of acquisition.

"I got rid of my psycho boss in the acquisition of our company," said his buddy, Craig. "Plus, I received stock options and a bump in pay from my new employer."

But Mike had no idea how the acquisition would impact him. These days, Mike tried to fall back asleep by watching *SportsCenter* on ESPN at 2:00 a.m. This had become somewhat of a habit the past few weeks since more changes went down at work.

Mike's wife, Sonja, had no idea he was not sleeping well; she was always a good sleeper. Their two girls, ages seven and three, shared a room down the hall, and Burt, their chocolate Labrador, slept soundly near Mike's feet.

Mike had a great marriage and family. He met Sonja at work sixteen years ago while working at the software company, Dreamsoft. Sonja was on the design team, and Mike was in IT. Mike found Sonja to be confident and comfortable with herself in the mostly male environment. It was pretty much love-at-first-meeting for Mike.

They were happy beyond measure when their daughter, Bella, came along seven years ago. Their joy quickly turned into dread when the doctors discovered that Bella had been born with an atrial septal defect, which required immediate heart surgery. Mike and Sonja watched as the cardiac team wheeled their tiny girl into surgery. Bella required weeks of hospitalization after her successful surgery and would need very close care for the next year.

Mike had returned to work two weeks after Bella's birth and was fortunate his boss, Albert, was completely supportive even though Mike was basically a zombie.

When Sonja's six-week maternity leave was almost up, she and Mike needed to make a decision.

"Should we hire a nurse-qualified nanny, or should one of us stay home for the next year until Bella is out of the woods?" asked Sonja.

They both earned a good salary from their jobs, so either of them could have become the main breadwinner. They decided that Sonja would stay home. Secretly, Mike was relieved that his wife was essentially taking one for the home team. He was immensely grateful.

The family fell into a nice routine over the next couple of years. Lea was born four years later, and Sonja taught a freshman-level coding class at the local junior college. Once she decided to go back to work full-time, she attacked the task with the same intensity she approached everything. She researched and networked and conducted informational interviews and was confidently unapologetic about having stayed home for seven years. After all, she had kept up on advances in her field of expertise, and the demand for her specific skill was very high in the current job market.

It felt like they could finally breathe at home. There was more money coming in, and everything just felt like it was falling into place. Mike and Sonja were a good team. And then Albert got fired so coldly and mysteriously. Suddenly Mike felt directionless.

Mike now regretted turning down a great job offer the previous year. Mike had been contacted by a recruiter representing a competitor and received an offer that would have increased his base salary by 25 percent. Mike and Sonja decided he would pass. The big reason he passed was that he was just thirteen months away from being vested in the company stock option at Bonzo. The stock could have meant a lot of money since Bonzo had experienced huge growth in the previous few years. Mike passed on the other role and would now live to regret it since Bonzo sold before he was vested, and MorTech would reset the vesting clock for all employees who stayed on. He felt like an idiot.

Sleep would not come that night for Mike. He didn't know it yet, but Mike had entered Crazytown.

CHAPTER 2

LIMBO LAND

Four weeks went by with absolutely no news about who would replace Albert as COO. Not a word.

Mike was astonished that the CEO of MorTech, John Boyd, had made such huge changes, impacting everyone in the company, yet communicated nothing. The weekly executive leadership meeting simply disappeared from Mike's calendar.

Out of desperation, Mike reached out to Albert but got an immediate text back from him saying that he and his wife were on a long-overdue extended trip to Europe and that he would reach out when he got back in a few months. Mike had not gone more than a week without talking to Albert in the past fourteen years, so the realization that he would not talk to Albert for months made his current reality even more unpleasant.

Mike's team was asking a lot of questions, but he could answer none of them because he had no information himself. Albert had taught Mike to carefully package information that could negatively impact people or their perceptions, but Mike had no information to package.

Mike tried to remain calm and simply encourage everyone, rather unconvincingly, to do their jobs well and to keep their heads down. He tried to tell himself the same thing.

The leaders at Bonzo had worked so hard to teach and to live the three company values of deliberation, transparency, and results, but that seemed to be gone now.

One day, Mike noticed someone was occupying Albert's office. He figured it was his new boss, but he was not about to ask. At that point, he wanted to see how long it would take for someone to reach out.

A few more people were let go during that time. Lena, the director of human resources, was released after eight years at Bonzo, and Robert, the chief financial officer, was let go as well. Mike figured these roles were redundant since MorTech had a huge HR department, and the MorTech CFO was probably a big part of the transaction to purchase Bonzo. Just like with Albert, there was a simple email and no "thanks for your service" or going-away parties. Nothing. Mike was slightly relieved to see that there was no CTO position listed on the MorTech website. But it seemed odd to Mike that he was both relieved that he might not be fired and yet felt a growing sense of not wanting his job anymore.

And then, five weeks to the day Albert was released, Mike got the following email.

Mike,

Please clear your schedule for Friday morning so that we can meet and discuss the following:

- Your team members' current salary and tenure

- Your team performance status against target

- Your department's financial performance for the past three years

- Current projects in the pipeline, as well as status reports on each major client

- Current status on your projects associated with The Hope Foundation

Donald Schiffman
Chief Operations Officer
MorTech Enterprises

The journey into Crazytown was about to get more intense.

CHAPTER 3

WAKE-UP CALL

Though Mike was in shock about the impersonal and direct tone of the email from his new boss, he decided to give the guy the benefit of the doubt. No mention of "nice to meet you" or "I am your new boss" or anything. Maybe the guy had forgotten his manners. Or, maybe he was a complete jerk, which is what he sounded like to Mike. Mike put his feelings aside and spent the rest of the week preparing for Friday's meeting.

Friday morning finally arrived, and Mike was in the office by 7:00 a.m. trying to mentally prepare for the unknown. He had slept like crap the night before—nothing new to him—and now he was as ready as he could be to meet with the new boss at 9:00 a.m.

Mike appeared in front of what used to be Albert's glass office but did not knock because there were two people in there, so Mike figured they were just finishing up. But the guy behind the desk waved him in, introduced himself as Donald Schiffman, and then introduced Mike to Derek

Miller, the VP of human resources, who would be joining them. Mike immediately wondered if they were going to fire him. The only time Mike included their former director of HR in a meeting was when it was time to let someone go. Mike felt numb.

Derek handed Mike a bound report titled "IT Department Status," which both Derek and Donald already had in front of them.

Donald said, "Okay, Mike, this is a complete report on your department. Let's dive in."

Mike took a deep breath and tried to stay focused. Over the next hour, they went through the report, which was the exact same info Mike had prepared. Why had he worked all week to answer the list of questions his new boss had asked him to bring to the meeting? What a waste of time when the HR guy was going to do it anyway.

Mike's department had performed well against target for the past three years. But Donald and Derek did not seem to care about past performance. Instead, they were very focused on the pipeline and the status report on each project Mike's team was working on. Mike felt uncomfortable but answered their questions as best he could.

It felt like the meeting was starting to wrap up when Donald told Mike he would need to cut his payroll overhead by 10 percent. Mike could not believe the words he just heard, so he asked, "Did you say 10 percent? Why?"

"MorTech has a strict policy of keeping payroll under 38 percent, and that means you need to cut the equivalent of 1.8 full-time people before the next payroll processes," said Donald. "You have two weeks from now to make it happen."

Mike was incredulous. He needed everyone on his team. His brain felt foggy, and all he could think to say was, "How do I get rid of 1.8 people? Have either of you seen eight-tenths of a person walking around here?"

Mike realized he was being sarcastic, but he was in shock and was trying not to lose it in front of his new boss and the HR guy.

"You'll figure it out," said Donald flatly.

And with that, Donald stood up and indicated that he and Derek had another meeting in a few minutes. No handshake, no thank you, no reassurance. On the way out, Mike gathered himself enough to mention that they had not discussed the current status of the Hope Foundation. He did not know it at the time, but later, he would regret this part of the meeting most.

The Hope Foundation was a passion project that Mike's idea had helped launch about five years prior. Bonzo collected old computers and laptops from their client base, providing Hope with materials that could be dissembled, recycled, and sold to fund the foundation. Hope employed 125 adults with autism and other disabilities to dismantle computers. It was Mike's pride and joy to host events and support Hope and their executive director, Lucinda, in every way that he could.

"Oh, thanks for reminding me," said Donald. "MorTech can't have one of its executives favoring a particular non-profit. Legal doesn't like it. It could be a liability. Frankly, I am surprised no one caught this before."

Mike no longer felt foggy. He now felt a surge of anger rise up in his throat. Bonzo's clients provided Hope with 90 percent of their materials, so this would mean the end of the foundation.

"But what about the adults with disabilities they employ?" asked Mike, not hiding his disgust. "This is a good thing we are doing, and our clients love being part of it," he said a bit too loudly, "and it is also pretty significant to 125 hardworking people!"

"Nonetheless," said Donald with a tone of finality.

Mike left the office, shaking his head with the word "nonetheless" ringing in his head. Nonetheless. None. The. Less.

"What a heartless idiot," Mike muttered to himself. "He's an idiot nonetheless."

Mike thought his career was a train wreck.

Little did Mike know, there was someone at MorTech who could help him get back on track and escape Crazytown.

CHAPTER 4

HOUSE HUSBAND

Mike left work in a daze after his meeting with Donald and Derek. Luckily, he had been able to avoid eye contact with his team for the remainder of the day. Mike did not have a good feeling about work and was in a state of disbelief at how rapidly his work life had changed.

Mike arrived at the after-school program to pick up the girls right at 5:30 p.m. The sight of his girls was a balm to his soul. Lea was smiling and skipping and holding her sister's hand as they raced to the door to greet Mike.

Sonja came home incredibly excited that she had been asked to visit her company's largest client in Japan. Sonja had studied Japanese in college but rarely got a chance to speak it. Visiting Japan was on her bucket list. Plus, it was a huge vote of confidence that her employer was sending her to work with their biggest client.

Sonja was killing it at work, and Mike's job was basically killing him.

Mike silently wondered if maybe he should just stay home and become a domestic dude, a house husband, or take a sabbatical or something.

Mike decided not to mention any of the work stuff to Sonja. Why ruin her great news with his giant bummer of a day?

CHAPTER 5

FIRE AWAY

Mike woke at 5:30 a.m. and realized he'd slept through the night for the first time in weeks. Maybe the beers he had the night before did the trick, or maybe his poor brain was in such shock that it did not have the energy to wake him up.

But there was no escaping from reality in the light of day. He had to find a way to step away from the meaningful employment of 125 disabled people and also fire people on his team.

Mike had fired a lot of people over the years. He had terminated a guy who was getting all of his work done but also watching internet pornography on his work computer for an impressive five hours a day. He'd had to fire two of his best IT support specialists for stealing company property—a huge roll of bubble wrap they stole after a work party one night. But he'd never let someone go without cause.

Mike decided that the logical decision would be to let Robert go. Not only was Robert the highest-paid in his department, which would get Mike to the 1.3 mark of the 1.8 requirement, but Robert was tough to work with. Truth be told, Mike had let Robert's antisocial behavior get out of hand. He refused to attend events or even most of Mike's meetings. Mike did not think Robert would be missed.

For the remaining .5 percent, Mike thought immediately of Shelia. After Shelia had a baby last year she had presented Mike with an excellent proposal to decrease her hours to part-time. Unfortunately, Bonzo had a strict no-part-time policy in IT at the time, so Mike had to decline. She took the news well, but Mike knew for a fact that she was still interested. First, he sent an email to the VP of HR and asked what MorTech's policy was on part-time workers and what the severance package would be for letting go of an eight-year employee.

CHAPTER 6

KINDERGARTEN, AGAIN

Mike stopped by Derek's office and explained that he had decided to meet the 1.8-person reduction requirement by laying off his top-paid team member and by cutting another to part-time. First, they went over the details of Shelia's change of status from full-time to part-time, which seemed to go smoothly. Mike was relieved.

Next, Mike explained that he would eliminate Robert's role and that Robert had been with the company for eight years, so they agreed on eight weeks of severance pay.

Derek pulled a piece of paper off his printer and explained to Mike that he was to say what was outlined there to Robert, and nothing more. Mike interrupted Derek to explain that he had been firing people since his first year at work and that he knew how to handle Robert; he would be fine.

Derek then said, "Let me be abundantly clear. This verbiage is what you are authorized to say. If you deviate from this script, you will likely hear from our in-house legal counsel, and I would not envy you if you cross them and put MorTech at risk for a lawsuit."

"What are you talking about?" Mike asked, incredulous. "I am an executive of this company, just like you are. Are you telling me that I cannot fire someone with my own words?"

"That is exactly what I am telling you," said Derek.

Mike looked at the piece of paper and read:

Due to a reduction in workforce, we are eliminating your position. Our policy is to offer one week of salary as severance for each year of your employment here, which is eight years to date.

In order to receive your severance, you will need to sign the statement below and agree not to discuss the terms of your departure with anyone.

Mike could not help but wonder if this was the "verbiage" Derek had used to fire Albert. It was cold and callous and inhumane, and it was not how Mike did business. Mike took a deep breath to gather himself. He then explained to Derek that Robert was a strange guy. Mike explained that Robert was quiet and kept to himself, but Mike suspected that underneath it all, Robert was a boiling cauldron of something unpleasant. Mike strongly urged Derek to consider making an exception in letting Mike deliver the news in a more humane way.

Mike said he would explain to Robert that he was excellent at his job but that he was sometimes hard to get along with and that he might want to work on that before taking his next role. Mike said he would like to give Robert a good reference.

Derek was even more deliberate and firm in his tone and leaned forward and enunciated clearly: "The way you describe this Robert guy is why you are only to say what is outlined in this script. I don't care if you need to read it to him verbatim. And for the record, what you just said is incredibly confusing legally. It sounds like you are releasing him for cause. And you are not. You will say nothing about offering a reference. All references come through my office, and we will give anyone who calls the date of hire, date of lay off, and eligibility for rehire. That's it," he said as if talking to a naughty kindergartener. "And I will be in that meeting with you, so be warned, if you deviate, I will take over the meeting."

Mike felt like he was in an alternate universe.

The meeting was set for the next morning. Much to Mike's surprise, Robert did not resist or become erratic. Mike simply followed the script and watched the reality register in Robert's eyes. He resisted the temptation to add any soothing words or reassurances, which was made easier by Derek's earlier threat to take over the meeting if he deviated. Robert hesitated for a long moment, signed the document, took his check, and left the meeting. His desk was cleaned out within the hour.

Mike messaged his team to gather for a meeting in conference room 1, where he explained that Robert was no longer working for MorTech and that Shelia would be working part-time starting next week. It occurred to him that he should address some of their silent concerns, but then they might ask questions he could not answer. He had no idea about the future, so what was the point of bringing it up?

CHAPTER 7

SAYONARA

The time for Sonja's trip had arrived, so Mike and the girls drove Sonja to the airport on Saturday morning. She would be gone for two weeks. That was longer than any of them had been apart since the girls were born. Mike had many five-to-six-day business trips, but Sonja had not taken one in over seven years, and Mike could tell she was worried about his ability to handle everything.

Mike had some of his own plans for the family during these two weeks. They would visit the Mobius Science Center and Children's Museum that day, and on Sunday, they would be the first in line at the Wonderland Family Fun Center.

Mike did not think about work once during the weekend. Sunday was especially fun. He immersed himself in Wonderland and let the girls choose what they wanted to do next. It felt great to be completely present for the girls, and they loved every minute of it.

Unfortunately, both girls woke in the night with a fever and what appeared to be the stomach flu. Not pleasant. The girls' fevers remained until Wednesday, long after every possible fluid was released from their little bodies. Luckily, he had a Shop-Vac plus Pedialyte and popsicles on hand (bless Sonja) and could keep them from becoming dehydrated. He was exhausted when he finally dropped the girls off at school on Thursday, just in time for Mike to feel the gurgling of his own stomach. He rushed home instead of driving to work. Mike felt like he'd been hit by a truck. He called his mother and reassured her the girls had recovered and asked her to pick them up from school and keep them until he recovered. He was so glad she immediately said yes. The last thing he wanted was to have the flu make its rounds again. Mike recovered in two days—just in time for the weekend, but had missed an entire week of work.

CHAPTER 8

FURY

Mike's mom dropped the girls off on Sunday morning. He and the kids watched movies and had a quiet afternoon. Mike decided to get some work done and deal with neglected emails. He had received 1,345 emails during his week away. He typed his new boss's name in the search field, and three emails popped up from Donald Schiffman. The second one caught his attention. The email was sent on Tuesday the previous week. It said:

Mike,

I met yesterday with Lucinda Riley, the executive director of the Hope Foundation. She seemed to have no idea that MorTech would be cutting ties with the non-profit this month. Isn't this your pet project? I assumed you would have put some kind of plan together by now or at least let the people know they needed a new partner.

DS

Anger surged through Mike's body. There was no previous email from Donald even asking about the foundation.

It was obvious to Mike that Donald had heard Mike was sick and decided to drive the stake further into his heart by meeting with Lucinda so that he could deliver the blow that Bonzo (now MorTech) would no longer host events or reach out to their customers for used electronics.

Mike actually had a few ideas up his sleeve, but with having to fire someone, all of the work changes, and then his household getting sick, he'd let it slip. Mike felt awful that Lucinda heard the news from cold Donald and not from him. He had not told her before because he was hoping to find a replacement source for the support role that Bonzo played. He also knew he was avoiding the whole reality of the foundation on some level because either way, his involvement would come to an end, and that was just too much to think about. Mike now had a sick feeling in his stomach as he dialed Lucinda's number to deal with this crisis created by his new boss.

Lucinda was understandably upset. Mike tried to listen and let her vent instead of whining about his work issues. Whatever his problems were, they were nothing compared to what Lucinda was facing if she had to shut down the foundation.

It turned out that Lucinda had rallied quickly and used her connections to get a meeting with The Gateway Foundation. Gateway was very well known in Washington state because of the tremendous goodwill that came from its work and mission. They loved the idea of absorbing Hope and would have much more access to tech company customers who would happily donate their used electronics to Hope. In the end, Lucinda had found herself a new tribe, and the Hope Foundation found a solid parent.

Mike hung up, feeling lost and unmoored.

CHAPTER 9

THE END OF AN ERA

When Mike pulled up to the house on the following Wednesday, his mother was sitting in her car in his driveway. Lilly Rogers was not the type to stop by without calling, so Mike wondered what was wrong. Lilly got out of the car and helped Mike get the girls out of their car seats and into the house. Mike and Lilly got the girls situated with a snack in the playroom before Mike could finally find out what was wrong.

"Honey, your dad has passed away," Lilly said with compassion. "One of his neighbors found him this morning." Mike's father, John, was a chronic alcoholic. He and Lilly had divorced when Mike and his sister Elaine were eight and ten years old. John was once a brilliant man and a talented architect. When John was not drinking, he was witty and charismatic and incredibly prolific in his work. Mike knew that he inherited his talent for programming and computer design from his dad's design genius. But when John was drinking, he became a different person. Both Mike and Elaine learned to become nearly invisible when that happened.

John's life had pretty much spiraled downhill after the divorce. Mike and Elaine had very little contact with John as adults. Mike had tried to reach out occasionally over the years, but it was too painful, and it always led to the same sad place. Mike and Sonja did not invite John to their wedding, and he had never met Bella and Lea. Mike thought he would feel relief when he heard about his dad's inevitable premature death. But Mike felt no relief at the news. He felt deeply, inexplicably disappointed.

Life was kicking Mike's butt, and he was wondering how much more he could take.

CHAPTER 10

THE FINAL STRAW

The next month was a blur for Mike. His boss actually seemed sympathetic when he found out Mike had lost his dad. Mike took a few days off when his sister arrived from Paris for the small memorial they held for John.

Both Mike's wife and mother encouraged him to talk to a therapist about his loss, especially given the combination of his dad being an alcoholic and all of the changes that were happening at work. But Mike did not feel like talking about it or reliving his childhood with some therapist. He decided work was the medicine he needed. So today, Mike busied himself with the prep for his client meeting in Chicago the next day.

Mike landed at O'Hare around 7:00 p.m. and had dinner in the bar at the Chicago Hilton. Mike was awakened at 1:30 a.m. by his heart, feeling like it was beating out of his chest with an elephant sitting on it. Mike stood up but had to sit right back down because he thought his head would burst. He was soaked with sweat.

This was a million times worse than anything he had ever experienced. *What the hell? Am I going to die in a hotel room at the ripe old age of forty-one?* His mind raced. Mike thought about calling an ambulance, but he just could not let himself create the drama of being wheeled out on a gurney. He called an Uber instead.

Mike managed to get into the Uber in spite of the terrible pain in his chest and was grateful he did not have to talk to the driver. The driver dropped him off at Northwestern Memorial Hospital emergency room just five minutes later. Despite the many people waiting in the busy emergency room, Mike's symptoms, and apparently his haunting appearance, got him immediate medical attention. The medical team set him up on an EKG machine and began asking about his medical history. The doctor ordered blood work, a chest x-ray, and an ultrasound. Within the hour, the tests were back, and the ER doctor let Mike know that he did not have a heart attack.

"You probably had an acute panic attack," said the ER doctor. "Is there any unusual stress going on in your life that could have contributed to this?"

Mike let out a loud, awkward laugh. "Uh, yes. The company I work for was acquired by jerks, my boss was fired, and my pathetic alcoholic dad died a couple of weeks ago." Mike felt immediate shame for sounding dramatic and for dissing his departed father.

"Well, panic attacks can look and feel like just a heart attack," the doctor replied. "I suggest you see your primary care physician when you get back home and get this treated. Some people also benefit from psychotherapy.

Once you have one panic attack, there is an increased possibility that you will have another one. Trust me; you don't want to leave this kind of thing unaddressed."

Mike completed the paperwork and silently admonished himself for the huge medical bill he would get for this little visit to an out-of-state ER. It would probably cost the equivalent of a family trip to Disneyland—all because he was a big crybaby and could not handle his life.

Mike was back in his hotel room by 4:00 a.m. He then showered and got ready for his 7:30 a.m. breakfast meeting with the client's IT team. The big meeting started at 10:00 a.m. No one seemed to notice that Mike felt like he had been through the wringer the night before and that he was operating with only half of his brainpower. He was grateful it was not a difficult client and extra grateful that his new boss was not going to be in the room. By 12:30 p.m., Mike was on his way to the airport for his 2:30 p.m. flight back to Spokane.

CHAPTER 11

ELIZABETH WALTON

Of course, his flight was delayed until 5:30 p.m. *Damn O'Hare on a Friday,* Mike thought. He called Sonja and deliberately tried to keep himself calm. He knew if he had one of the panic attacks at the gate before his flight, that he would never be allowed to board. Beer! He needed beer and food and headed for the Chili's near his gate and asked to be seated in the back. He had time to kill, and he needed to regroup.

Mike caught a glimpse of himself in the mirror as he walked past the bar and realized he actually *did* look as bad as he felt. He ordered a beer and a double bacon cheeseburger and fries with queso and chips as an appetizer—after all, hadn't the doctor said his heart was fine? He pulled out a notepad intending to make a list of the changes he needed to make in his life. But his brain was not working. He felt like hell. He felt confusion, but mostly, he felt pathetic. He was so embarrassed about the previous night that he wasn't even sure he would tell Sonja.

When the server brought his food, he ordered another beer, and then he heard someone ask, "Bad day at the office?" He looked up and noticed a sharply dressed woman talking to him. She looked vaguely familiar.

"You are Mike Rogers, the head of IT, right?" she stuck her hand out to Mike. "I am Elizabeth Walton, the CFO of MorTech." Mike had seen her name on the website but had never met her or even talked to her. Mike immediately straightened up and started to make excuses for his appearance and the massive amount of food in front of him. Elizabeth caught on immediately and said, "At ease, soldier. We're in an airport, not at the office. Do you mind if I join you?"

Mike said sure since he felt he had no choice.

Elizabeth ordered a bacon cheeseburger, a salad, and a Grey Goose Cosmopolitan.

"Hey, we're both delayed; may as well get to know each other. By the way, you look awful. Are you okay?"

Mike laughed and told her she did not want to know.

"Well, you don't have to be an investigator to put it together. Let's see, your company got acquired, your boss gets fired, you get a new boss, your foundation involvement is canceled, you had to make cuts to your team, and then your dad dies. Does that about sum it up?"

Mike felt his eyes burning. His Adam's apple ached. Hearing the list of things that had happened in his life listed outside of his own head had an unwelcome impact on him. He felt like he was going to cry, so instead, he made fun of himself.

"You forgot to add that I thought I was having a heart attack in the middle of the night last night and went to the ER," said Mike. "It turns out I now have panic attacks, and I am crazy or something. Look out, I could lose it again right here, and then you would really have something to tell Donald and John in your next executive committee meeting."

"Well, I am sorry to hear about the panic attack, and I am very sorry to hear about your dad. But please know that I would never, ever share something told to me in confidence. Ever."

Something about Elizabeth made Mike believe her.

"I had a panic attack once," she said casually. "I was at work, in my last job before MorTech, and someone called an ambulance. It was dreadful. I thought I was having a heart attack because there was an invisible anvil on my chest. I learned later that it was only my train wreck of a life that caused my body to rebel against me, not my heart. But people treated me differently at work after that. It was not a good chapter in my life."

"How did you keep it from happening again?" Mike asked immediately.

Elizabeth let out a loud laugh. "That, my friend, is the million-dollar question! You can let things get a lot worse as I did, and then be forced to change your life in every imaginable way, or you can take the warning your body and mind gave you very seriously and change things now."

Elizabeth's burger arrived, and she asked Mike if he wanted to hear her story. He really did.

CHAPTER 12

TRUE CONFESSIONS

"Mike, I promise you that you are not the only person who is having a rocky and punishing phase in your career. And you are right on time with your age too. What are you, forty-something?"

"Forty-one."

"Yep. It is the perfect storm," Elizabeth went on. "It feels like your brain and your heart are at odds. You feel confused and unhappy but cannot seem to shake it or even really figure out why it's all happening to you. It is supremely uncomfortable. You are wondering if you need a change and where the meaning is. Thinking maybe you should take a sabbatical or something. I always say it's in our forties when we lose our ability to tolerate the intolerable. Your preferences seem to be changing. You might be wondering if you are in a midlife crisis or something like that."

Mike agreed with everything Elizabeth said, but he felt extremely confused as to how she could know all of this.

He looked around the restaurant to see if there were some cameras or if he was being "punked" or tricked. How bizarre it was that this senior executive from his company somehow knew his life and was articulating it in a way that he had yet to articulate it himself. It felt creepy but somehow validating.

"What if I told you what is going on with you is a gift of sorts?"

"I would laugh in your face," Mike retorted.

"Well, if you can be okay for a while longer with the discomfort and figure things out for yourself, this messy stage could really be what keeps you from having an actual midlife crisis in the future. But we can talk more about that later. First, I will tell you my story.

"I am about twelve years older than you, Mike. And up until my forties, my career was a hard-earned rise from one top position to another. I worked on Wall Street for Goldman Sachs, Leman Brothers, Morgan Stanley, the list goes on. I learned to compete in a male-dominated industry by using my analyst capabilities and simply ignoring anything that got in the way of my success. It worked very well, but that skill of ignoring my surroundings would cost me later.

"I have two children who are now in their twenties and thriving. But in my early forties, my marriage failed. Long story, but I was having my own little crisis. I decided I wanted to do something very different, so I left New York and moved my family back to Washington state and went to work for a tech startup. It sounded so exciting to use my analyst skills for this one company and possibly a big paycheck if we succeeded in selling the company in three years as planned.

"The founder was charismatic beyond anything I had ever experienced. The technology was revolutionary, and the investors were completely committed to our success. Because it was a startup, we all had many jobs. I was not only the CFO but the controller as well. I had not put together a set of financials since I got my CPA license many years prior, so it was kind of fun. And in a lot of ways, it was more aligned with my values of containing costs and not wasting money. Wall Street was all about decadence and excess, which I never felt quite aligned with.

"Things were great for the first year. The nineteen of us were like family. In retrospect, it was at about the one-year mark that some changes happened with the founder, but I did not notice it at the time. We were in the midst of our second big round of funding. The founder started working around the clock. He had developed kind of an edge, and he was starting to demand more of the rest of the team and me.

"One night, when I was paying the company bills, I noticed something weird about the recurring invoice we were paying to a vendor. The weird feeling turned out to be suspicion, and that suspicion lead me to the worst possible scenario. The vendor was, in fact, owned by the founder, and it appeared as if we were funneling tens of thousands of dollars to this company, which was not providing any service whatsoever to ours.

"I started digging into everything. What I found was a huge web of corporate malfeasance. The founder had paused payments on many of the company's insurance policies, which left us open for liability and stopped paying into the 401K fund. He was careful not to touch any of the items I handled, so at least the healthcare premiums were getting paid, and we made payroll each month. But it was a mess.

"I spent the next week secretly gathering evidence and reached out to a Stanford alumni friend, who was a big corporate attorney. He agreed that I needed to confront the founder and that if he refused to come clean with the board, then I would inform the board of what I had discovered. When I met with the founder and showed him what I had, he flew into a rage. He fired me on the spot. It was the night before his next big board meeting. When I told him that I would go to the board, he laughed like a crazy person and said they would never believe me."

"What?" Mike interrupted, "He couldn't just fire you, right? Did you sue him?"

"Yes, he could do it, and he did. I had no employment contract. And whatever he said to the board that night convinced all of them to refuse to take my calls. As I said before, this guy could sell it. And as you know, we are an 'at will' employment state, so there I was: fired, with only two weeks' severance, and humiliated. In those two years working for him, I had essentially neglected my kids by working around the clock for nothing while unwittingly helping a corporate criminal perpetrate a crime on his investors and his employees."

"Is that when you went to work for MorTech?"

"I wish! No, no, it would be nearly two years before I landed at MorTech as I had not yet reached rock bottom. I was in such shock and shame over what happened that I immediately signed up with Account-Temps and took a job working on tax returns for one of their clients. It was a huge mistake on many levels. First of all, it was about ten levels below where I belonged, but nobody knew me, and nobody cared about my stellar career. And I did not really care, either. My confidence was shot, and I was obsessed with the idea of keeping money coming in.

"I was there about six months when the whole I-think-I'm-having-a-heart-attack thing happened to me in the middle of a workday. The emergency room doctor told me it was time to reevaluate my life, and she was absolutely right. It was about a week after my little incident, and people were treating me like I was radioactive. I do not fault them; I had not connected emotionally with one single person in six months. I was a burned-out mess. So, I handed in my resignation and packed up what few items I had and walked out. Not my proudest professional moment."

"If you are saying all of this to make me feel better, it's working. I can't believe you were going through all that and single-parenting as well. My issues are nothing as serious as what you experienced. I am happily married, and my family is my rock right now, and I do still have a job. How the heck did you go from there to where you are now?"

"First of all, don't dismiss what you are experiencing. It is every bit as stressful for you as it was for me because it is happening to you. And secondly, the way I got through it was what I learned when I studied psych as an undergrad.

It's referred to as 'doing the work.' Fortunately, I had some savings, and I decided not to get a new job again until I did some work on myself.

"Over the next twelve months, I went to a therapist, hired a trainer, and lost twenty-five pounds. I organized every physical aspect of my life—I even cleaned out the jam-packed tool shed on my property and spent lots of money to have my kitchen remodeled—my lifelong dream. I cleaned every closet and drawer in my house and got rid of clothes and stuff I had been accumulating my entire adult life. I donated over five hundred books. Within a year of leaving the startup job, I had dipped into as much of my savings as I was comfortable with, so I started a job search. Unfortunately, that damn startup on my résumé foiled me at every turn, and I was not finding what I knew was right; I was not getting interviews for the roles at appropriate levels. I wasn't even getting past the initial screening calls.

"So, then, I hired a career coach. She put me through a series of tests and helped me deal with what she called my 'career baggage.' And oh, was there some baggage—going all the way back to Wall Street. The therapist I saw was great about helping me explore why my marriage ended and how to reconnect with my children and myself. It was incredibly helpful. The career coach helped me figure out my blind spots and my responsibility in all of the career mess. Then, she taught me how to talk about the startup debacle in a way that did not set off alarm bells in the minds of recruiters and executives interviewing me. It took about six months to find the role at MorTech, and I have been happy here doing mergers and acquisitions and heading up their treasury department as well. It's been eight years since all of that happened, and I have never been happier."

"Wow," said Mike. "That is quite a story. So, are you suggesting I quit MorTech and clean out my shed?"

Elizabeth smiled. "One thing you will find out if we become friends is that I hardly ever give advice, but I can offer some assistance. Each year since I have been at MorTech, I have chosen someone to mentor. It's usually someone from my professional network back in New York or a connection from the university where I teach a graduate class on finance. But I only take on one person per year. My criteria are that they are at least thirty-five years old, in a professional career and in a bit of a crisis, and most importantly, are willing to do the work. I like you, Mike. I sense you have a lot of game, and I would like to offer you my assistance."

Mike felt a bit self-conscious. "Um, what would that cost, and how would that work given that you are a senior executive and board member of the company I work for?"

"The way it works is that we meet twice a month for about sixty minutes, and there is no charge," said Elizabeth.

"That's a pretty big commitment on your part. Why would you do that?" asked Mike.

"It is my way of giving back. I was very fortunate that I had the financial means to quit my job, hire help, and figure myself out. I realize very few people can do that. So, I get a lot out of the work. You can think about it and email me Monday. Talk to your wife about it. If you are game, I will email you a nondisclosure agreement. It will contain my agreement to keep the content of our meetings confidential, and you agree to not sue MorTech based on anything that we discuss. Oh, and there is no obligation for you to stay at MorTech as a result of our work. No strings attached.

"Now, I think our flight is boarding, so let's get home." Elizabeth paid the tab, then she and Mike shook hands and headed toward the gate.

Mike had a story to tell his wife. There just might be a way out of Crazytown.

CHAPTER 13

DATE NIGHT

Mike got home from Chicago after midnight and was awakened at 7:00 a.m. by two girls very excited to see their daddy. At that moment, he regretted teaching them the concept of "dog pile" as his bed became a trampoline of hands and legs landing on him. He commenced the tickling, and the squealing reached deafening levels.

Sonja came in and settled the girls and handed Mike a cup of coffee. "I have been keeping them away from you for over an hour. I'm sorry, but they missed you very much. And so did I for some reason," she jokingly said as she leaned in for a kiss.

"Do we have any birthday parties today?" Mike asked sheepishly.

"Actually, no, why do you ask?" said Sonja.

"Well, I would like to take my family to breakfast, and then tonight, if we can get my mom to come by, could we go on a grown-up date?"

"Sure," said Sonja. "But is everything okay? You seem different."

"Everything is fine. I need to fill you in on some stuff about work, and we have not had a date in a long time. A lot has happened. Let's see if we can get a reservation at Churchill's and take our time and have a nice dinner."

"Churchill's, really? Did you get a raise or something?" joked Sonja. They both laughed. Sonja wrangled the girls while Mike called his mother and checked the app for reservations at Churchill's, a local fancy steakhouse.

Later at the restaurant, they toasted to the girls, and Mike began to fill Sonja in on the details of the past few months. He told her about his disdain for Donald, his new boss. How he had been forced to make unfair reductions for the first time in his career and how humiliated he was that Lucinda found out about the foundation changes from Donald instead of Mike while the girls were sick.

He explained how he was feeling disconnected from his work and how weird it was to not talk to Albert. He confessed he had not been sleeping much since the acquisition and that he feared MorTech was not the kind of company he wanted to invest the rest of his career in, and he admitted to doubting everything work-related and feeling confused and embarrassed.

Then he reluctantly told Sonja about what happened in Chicago—waking up with his heart pounding, sweating profusely, and going to the ER. Sonja's eyes welled up with tears as she listened to Mike talk about the tests he took and the relief of learning that he was not, in fact, having a heart attack, and how humiliated he felt when he found out it was a panic attack. Mike paused as he could tell Sonja was becoming very upset.

He waited for Sonja to compose herself. She looked around the restaurant and then leaned forward tearfully and whispered, "You took an Uber to the hospital when you thought you had a heart attack? What was the Uber driver supposed to do if you had an actual heart attack in the back seat? We could have lost you, Mike. The girls and I could have lost you!"

Sonja took a deep breath. "Mike, I need you to promise me right now that you are going to take better care of yourself. And that if you ever, ever again, suspect you are experiencing a life-threatening illness that you will do everything in your power to survive for our family, and that would include taking an actual ambulance to the hospital, if necessary. Do you promise?"

Mike said yes.

Then Sonja shocked Mike by telling him he should quit MorTech. She reminded him that they had lived on one salary for seven years, and they could do it again. Mike was surprised that Sonja was so supportive and pretty happy that their date was not over. It felt really nice. Then he told her about meeting Elizabeth and that she offered to mentor him with no strings attached. They googled Elizabeth together and were blown away by her bio.

"Wow!" said Sonja. "She sounds pretty impressive."

"Yeah, she does," said Mike. "I think she has had a career hiccup or two not mentioned in the bio you read. But that is why she mentors one person each year, I guess."

Mike felt intensely relieved he had shared his story with Sonja. He should have trusted her sooner and not suffered in silence. Mike had some decisions to make over this weekend. He and Sonja decided they were too tired for dessert and called an Uber to take them home.

CHAPTER 14

STRESS FANTASIES

Mike drove to work Monday morning wondering if he should take a leap and finally open that kayak shop he had always dreamed of near Silver Lake. Mike had been a competitive kayak racer in high school and worked in a shop where he gave lessons to earn money every summer for four years. His mind drifted to the image of living in sports clothes every day, the simplicity of teaching people how to kayak, helping them choose the best one, and earning money that way. No meetings, no mergers and acquisitions, no mysterious anxiety attacks.

When Mike got to his desk, he found Elizabeth Walton's email in the directory and sent her an email thanking her for dinner, for her time, and letting her know that he would like to accept her offer for mentoring.

Elizabeth replied immediately and sent the necessary documents which Mike signed and returned. She asked him to book a room for ninety minutes at the local library Friday morning at 7:00 a.m. and to send her a calendar invite. She explained that if all went well, they would meet every other Friday for sixty minutes at the library. Mike could not imagine what they would discuss or what advice she would give him about his flailing career.

At 7:00 a.m. on Friday, Elizabeth appeared in the room Mike reserved at the library and shook his hand. "Congratulations!" she said.

"For what?" Mike asked. "I haven't done anything yet."

"Mike, you have made a move forward; you have trusted someone to help you, and you showed up today. Coaching and mentoring are all predicated on the theory that in spite of where you are currently in life, there is always a way to move forward. Psychotherapy, conversely, is about healing the past and reflecting on why we do certain things. I am a big fan of therapy; it saved me when I was in a fragile state. Therapy asks questions like, 'Why do I do that?' or 'Where did that behavior come from?' Those are very important and useful directions to explore, but coaching never asks why we do what we do or where that behavior comes from. Instead, coaching or mentoring helps us acknowledge the unpleasant place where we find ourselves and figure out how we can incrementally move forward. It's hard to do that on your own. You are doing something that your future self will thank you for doing. By being willing to look at yourself and improve behaviors, you are placing yourself in a rare percentage of people. That, sir, is why I congratulated you."

Mike was slightly intrigued.

"So normally, I would ask you to start by telling me your career story," continued Elizabeth, "but I know a lot of your story, and so I think we can dive right in."

Mike pulled out his phone to take some notes, but Elizabeth made it abundantly clear that there would be no electronics in their sessions, and unless there was some family medical reason, there were to be no audible notifications interrupting their mental focus. She handed Mike a legal pad and pulled out one for herself.

Elizabeth settled into her seat. "I am guessing that you are considering options outside of MorTech, is that correct?" Mike was a little surprised at how direct Elizabeth was and that she went right to that point.

"What are some of your ideas?" she asked.

Mike was visibly uncomfortable as he responded. "Um, well, I am not sure the culture of MorTech is for me. I mean, I talked to Sonja over the weekend, and we could afford for me to quit for a while. Well, not forever, as we have two bright girls who are going to need to go to college, and we will want to retire someday. Maybe I just need to work somewhere that has more meaning for me. Or, I could just stick it out for another fifteen years and stay where I am. MorTech will probably get sold, and I will make a lot of money. But the meaning is gone for me. I really loved the responsibilities of the Hope Foundation, and now that is gone, too.

"I sometimes wonder if I should go do IT for a nonprofit or something. I mean, what am I really contributing to the world now? I sit in my car for about twenty minutes every day outside of MorTech, and for the first time in my life, I don't want to go in. It's kind of crushing my soul. I know my team deserves better, but for some reason, I cannot motivate myself to be a good leader to them. Oh, God, I am rambling. I am so sorry."

"First of all, rambling is good. That stream of consciousness is very helpful to our cause here. Think about it: when do we ever get to talk out loud and uninterrupted in life?"

Mike felt an odd sense of relief. He had just said things to Elizabeth that he had never said out loud.

Encouraged, Mike continued. "What I really want to do is to open a kayak shop at Silver Lake. I used to compete and teach lessons in high school. I know there are quite a few shops serving that lake, but I could really differentiate my shop with my teaching method."

"Thanks for telling me all of that, Mike. It really helps me to understand a little bit about where you are coming from," said Elizabeth. "Let me frame a few things that might be useful for you.

"First of all, it's kind of a jungle out there in the corporate world, so I want you to know that you are not imagining it. Have you ever heard of the term VUCA?"

Mike shook his head.

"It's actually an Army term, but it fits for the corporate world perfectly. VUCA stands for volatility, uncertainty, complexity, and ambiguity. The volatility can come from ups and downs of the world markets and investor expectations, which put ridiculous pressure on quarterly earnings, and the environment of mergers and acquisitions puts so much pressure on leadership that it creates a sort of insanity in the work environment. Uncertainty comes from most of us not knowing what will happen in our work and our careers. Nothing about our work is as simple as it was in prior generations. The complexity comes from the type of problems that we need to solve, plus the political dynamics of our work. And all of that creates a sense of ambiguity. Most people have no idea what their future career path is and where they fit into the vision of the company. Being able to thrive in ambiguity will be the top skill of the future for anyone who is going to stay in the corporate world."

This made perfect sense to Mike.

Elizabeth paused and then went on. "I call it Crazytown. Crazytown is not really a word unless you consult the Urban Dictionary, but for me, it describes things well. I mention this to you, Mike because I don't want you to feel crazy for being unhappy. But I also need you to know that there is no simple answer to getting away from it."

It was clear that Mike wanted to hear more.

"Crazytown is not just here at MorTech," continued Elizabeth. "And there is no ideal company where all of your needs will be met, either. If you are going to change companies, it will be because you have examined the trade-offs, and you prefer the trade-offs of a new venture over the current ones you are making."

"Or, I could just go work for a nonprofit," said Mike.

"So many corporate professionals think that the answer is 'go and work for a nonprofit.' Nonprofits are not exempt from Crazytown behaviors. I have grad students who work for nonprofits, and some of their stories are as bad or worse than the horror stories I hear at multi-billion-dollar companies.

"And I support you 100 percent if your dream is to open a kayak shop," continued Elizabeth. "But one thing we need to determine together is if that is a concrete idea that could be profitable and actually provide meaning to you, or if it is a stress fantasy."

Mike chuckled and asked, "Stress fantasy? What is that?"

"A stress fantasy is something that sounds good, but does not really have the teeth to succeed when looked at logically," said Elizabeth. "Mike, right now, it's like you have your hand on a hot stove. Taking your hand off that stove sounds so good that you will do almost anything to feel relief. But relief is not a good indicator of a correct decision because these are complex issues, and the relief will only be short term. A year from now, you do not want to be right back where you are today, but hundreds of thousands of dollars in debt. Or at some other company where you are even more miserable. Not ideal."

"So, I am trapped!" said Mike dramatically.

"No, you are certainly not trapped," said Elizabeth emphatically. "You have more options than you can imagine right now, but you'll need to commit the time to explore and figure things out. It's a process, and there are no simple, quick answers. Also, you are not old by any stretch of the imagination, but you are not twenty-five years old, either. Your moves at this age are critical and come with consequences. Twenty-somethings can change career lanes and explore new avenues all they want without long-term consequences. Your options are narrower than they were in your twenties, but you also have more leverage now than you did in your twenties, which we will talk about later."

"So, is this what you are going to help me with?" asked Mike. "Because I have no idea how to proceed."

"Yes, that is what we will be doing in our sessions," said Elizabeth enthusiastically. "When I had my own mid-career crisis, I developed a success philosophy that boiled down to four major buckets or keys."

Elizabeth held up her index finger. "The first bucket is stress. You need to learn how to deal with stress like a boss, as they say. I do love the Urban Dictionary. Boss refers to someone who knows what they want and finds a way to get it. The external and internal stress of today's world requires different coping strategies than our parents' generation could have ever imagined. Dealing with stress like a boss means understanding your own wiring, a bit of brain science, and a willingness to really know yourself."

Mike raised his eyebrows.

"The second bucket is to figure out your career superpower. The career superpower is a way of looking at your unique strengths; what you bring to the table no matter what you do—and how you do it better than others in your space. Your career superpower is about how you solve problems, what your unique opinions are, and the values that you bring to work. Have you ever given that any thought?"

"No," said Mike plainly. "Never."

"You are not alone; most of us just go from one thing to the next in our careers without a lot of thought." Elizabeth held up three fingers now and smirked a little. "The third bucket is about identifying your blind spots. I know right now you are focused on Donald's leadership style and behaviors that you do not care for, but you will want to get some perspective about your own communication style and habits. Is there a gap between the leader that you can be and the leader that you actually are? Even if you leave MorTech, you don't want to take any bad habits with you, right?"

Mike agreed.

"The fourth bucket is activating your network as a form of career leverage. Your professional network is your career insurance. You probably have a bigger network than you think, and we will improve and deepen that. The adage about saving money applies perfectly to building and nurturing a professional network. The best time to start saving for retirement is twenty years ago. But the second-best time is today. Same goes with your network."

Mike was almost animated when he said, "Yeah, that is what I need. I need to work on my network. You are so right. Can we start there?"

Elizabeth burst out laughing. "I am not laughing at you," she continued. "I am laughing because everyone I have ever mentored wants to start with their network, of course. Who wants to deal with stress and finding their blinds spot? No one! But, Mike, we don't want to activate or even begin to develop your network until we know what you want to do with your career. And we cannot really figure out what you want while you are not sleeping and having panic attacks. Capiche?"

Mike nodded.

"I am saying we have a little bit of work to do in the other areas first. Agreed?"

"Yes."

"I have some assessments for you to complete, and then that wraps things up for today," said Elizabeth. Mike could not believe the time went by so quickly.

"But first, I would like you to synopsize for me what was helpful today. I will ask you this at the end of every session we have because it will help your brain kind of organize its files and catalog your learning, which is all part of the incremental change we talked about."

Mike took a deep breath and said, "Well, I learned that we are going to work on my ability to deal with stress and my superpowers and what my blind spots are, and then on my professional network. And that maybe opening a kayak shop is a stress fantasy. And that VUCA thing." He glanced at his notes. "Volatility, uncertainty, complexity, and ambiguity are rampant in today's world, so I cannot just find a different place and expect everything to be rosy. And that is about it."

"Great job," said Elizabeth. "I am glad to hear you got so much out of our first session. And back to the stress bucket. I do have a little homework for you." Mike had his pen at the ready.

"How much are you exercising right now?" asked Elizabeth.

Mike was surprised at her question. "Well, not at all. I have not gone for a run or to the gym in at least six months."

"Your homework is to start working out again. It does not matter what you do, but I suggest you choose what sounds the most pleasant to you. What would that be?"

"Running, for sure. I love running, and Burt, our dog, loves it, too. I just got out of the habit. I don't know what happened."

"Life happens!" said Elizabeth. "Now, how many times a week and what distance could you start doing with 100 percent certainty? I want you to think before you answer. It is really important that you do not set any goals for yourself that you are not 100 percent sure you can accomplish. This means you have to set the bar low. Our culture likes to tell us to set big, audacious goals and to push ourselves. This is the opposite of how the reward center works in the human brain."

"I could do two days a week and easily get in a few miles each time. I could be back before the girls leave for school and could go Monday, Wednesday, or Friday."

"Okay, that is your homework. And it will be your job to let me know if you did it or not. I am not your accountability police officer. You are a grown man, and you have a big life. I am not interested in adding any more pressure to your life. If you do it, great. If not, try again next week. It is that simple," Elizabeth said.

"Sounds good," said Mike. "See you in two weeks. And thank you. I don't know why, but I feel somehow hopeful. Thanks a lot for taking the time to work with me."

"I am very glad to hear it, Mike," said Elizabeth. "And you are very welcome." She thought about the topic of their next session and chuckled to herself; Mike might not be so grateful when he hears what they would cover next.

CHAPTER 15

GOING TO THE UGLY

Two weeks later, Mike pulled up to the library at the same time Elizabeth was getting out of her Lexus LX. She looked professional in a dress, jacket, and designer shoes. Mike had been around women enough to know expensive clothes when he saw them, and Elizabeth was wearing some nice duds.

"Wow, you look nice!" said Mike.

"Thank you, Mike. I am giving the opening keynote at a woman's conference this afternoon, so I will head over there after our session today to rehearse a bit and set up my AV. So, if it's okay, we will be done in forty-five minutes today."

"How do you have time for all that you do, plus serve as the CFO and treasurer at MorTech, teach at the university, sit on boards, and all of that?" asked Mike.

Elizabeth responded, "I am very good with my time. It is one of my career superpowers, and we will discuss yours at some point. But mostly, Mike, my kids are grown. I am pretty much free to do as I please. You and Sonja are in the thick of it with your current age and stage. It's very hands-on at this juncture, and it's both wonderful and very time-consuming. You won't even realize how busy you are now until the girls start driving, and then you will wonder how you did it all."

Mike bristled at the thought of Bella or Lea operating a two-ton vehicle.

"But there is no use projecting that far ahead," continued Elizabeth as they walked into their reserved room. "Suffice it to say that even as busy as I am, I have a lot more free time than you do. So, update me, Mike. How are things going?"

Mike pulled out the new leather-bound notebook he purchased for taking notes during his sessions with Elizabeth.

"I have been running every day. Except for the last two Sundays, I have run five miles a day, every day. It feels great. I can't believe how much I missed it. And our dog, well, he's happy too. On Saturdays, I take Bella with me for part of the run. She is old enough to learn a few running techniques, and she loves it," beamed Mike.

"Mike, that is great news," said Elizabeth. "I am so glad you picked a goal that you knew you could deliver on, and I am not surprised that you are doing even more than you had hoped for. One of the reasons it is so important to under-promise and over-deliver to ourselves is explained in very recent, groundbreaking brain science. The neuroscience experts tell us that the brain does not discern between a good habit and a bad habit. For example, if you have a habit of shooting heroin into your arm every day, and that heroin did not kill you yesterday, your brain will encourage you to do it again today. There is a reward center of your brain that bathes your brain with happy chemicals like dopamine and serotonin, and those chemicals encourage us to do what we usually do, again and again."

Mike's eyes widened.

"So, when we are trying to create a new habit like exercising more or improving any aspect of our lives, we tend to overshoot on the goal and end up not doing what we said we would do. Because it is a new habit, there is no happy chemical reaction, so we miss our goal, and we feel terrible. But if we set a lower goal, one we are more likely to reach, the brilliant neuroplasticity of the brain creates a new pathway over time, and soon will give you the dopamine and serotonin for that new habit and decrease the happy chemicals for the 'bad' habit you no longer do regularly, which in your case, was not exercising."

Mike's mind shifted to his father, who was plagued by his love for alcohol most of Mike's life. He had attended a few Al-Anon meetings before he and Sonja married to try to learn a little bit about his father's disease. He vaguely recalled learning something like what Elizabeth was explaining.

"So, it is like a positive addiction?" asked Mike.

"Yes! We basically program our brains with either good or bad habits," she said. "We left off last time talking about the four ways we fortify ourselves against the whole reality of corporate Crazytown. Today, I would like to delve into the stress part a bit. You have given yourself a great start at managing stress like a boss because you are exercising. In today's business culture and lifestyle, physical exercise is more like a prescription than a luxury. Physical exercise is a critical component in managing stress. Now let's go a level deeper and talk about what I call professional baggage."

"Okay," said Mike hesitantly. "Do I seem like I have professional baggage?"

"Yes, yes, you do," Elizabeth said flatly. "But don't feel bad, everyone does. And because we don't want you to be carrying that 'baggage' into every aspect of your future career, we need to deal with it; I am going to teach you a little game called 'Going to the Ugly.'"

Mike chuckled nervously.

"I want you to think about your refrigerator for a minute. Imagine you have a Tupperware container hidden in the back of the fridge from six months ago. You know the contents of that container are nasty. Probably moldy and stinky, right? So, let's call the container, 'My new boss, Donald.'"

Mike agreed reluctantly, not knowing where she was going with this analogy.

"When it comes to that container, there is no amount of positive thinking or denial that is going to make that gunk in the container go away. Our business culture tells us to be positive or to not think about the bad stuff in the container. But the only way to deal with what is in that container is to open it up and wash it out, right?"

"Right..." said Mike, with a sideways glance.

"So that is what we are going to do. Now, keep in mind there will always be a container called 'My new boss, Donald.' We cannot make it go away entirely, because this is your mind we are talking about. But once we clean it out, it will have a lot less power over you. Make sense?"

"Sort of."

"Okay," said Elizabeth, reaching for a legal pad. "I am going to set a timer for five minutes. In these five minutes, I want you to complain bitterly about Don, and I will write as fast as I can. I want you to set aside your manners and the whole concept of taking responsibility for your part in things and just complain. Rant and rave if you like. Got it?"

"Um, okay," said Mike. "But I don't know if I have five minutes' worth."

"You will be surprised once you get warmed up," said Elizabeth. "Ready? Set, go."

Mike started reluctantly, "Well, he was in his office for weeks and never even introduced himself, and then he sent me a terse email and gave me a list of stuff to bring. I prepped all week for that first meeting, but he and the new HR guy had all of the information anyway. What a waste of time. They completely railroaded me in that meeting too."

Elizabeth noticed that Mike's face was a bit red. "You're doing great. Now keep going but tell it to me in the form of a list—not a story, you still have four-and-a-half minutes."

Mike took a deep breath and continued:

"He's heartless.

"He made me give up the Hope Foundation. He's a jerk.

"He made me cut 1.8 people. Who says that? Who does that?

"He does not talk to me.

"I could be doing nothing all day, and he would never notice.

"I have no idea what the vision of MorTech is.

"He went behind my back when my kids were sick and met with Lucinda just to spite me.

"He only cares about my new business and never acknowledges my successful history.

"He and the CEO did not even acknowledge Albert and his commitment to the company.

"I hate the new culture.

"He and that Derek guy from HR seems to be buddy-buddy. I don't trust them.

"And what are the new company values? MorTech certainly does not value deliberation, transparency, and results!" Mike spat the words and just sat there for a moment.

"Okay, good job," said Elizabeth in a soothing tone. "If we have done this right, you probably feel worse right now than you did when we started."

"Yep, if I am supposed to get all worked up, I am!" Mike said, embarrassed.

"You are doing great," said Elizabeth. "Now, take a deep breath and tell me what the worst part of all of this is."

Mike's face darkened, and he answered right away. "It's all so different. It is like my life changed overnight."

"Okay, stay with me," said Elizabeth. "I am going to ask you some questions, and then you might see the method to my madness."

Elizabeth put the legal pad of Mike's complaints in front of him.

"For this next step, I want you to pretend you are someone else now. Read through this situation as if you happened upon it. What do you notice?"

Mike read the page of complaints.

"I'd say this guy sounds lost and angry."

"Okay, good. If you had a magic wand, what would you change about all of this?"

Mike sighed. "I would bring Albert back and make Donald disappear." Mike hesitated. "But Albert probably got a huge payout from the sale, and he probably doesn't have to work anymore if he doesn't want to. He's older than I am, and maybe he doesn't mind being gone, even if he didn't get a going-away party. I just miss him."

"So, Mike, if you looked at this whole situation with a lot of compassion for yourself, what might you notice?"

"I guess I would notice that there has been a lot of change in a short period of time, both at home and at work. My wife went back to work after seven years; my boss disappears; my dad dies. It's a lot of change," said Mike quietly.

"And tell me, what you have tried to do to deal with all of this change, Mike?"

"I have mostly tried to just suck it up and ignore it. I have tried to be calm and not lose my temper. I have tried to stay somewhat connected to my team, though I am earning poor marks in that department lately. And I guess I have just hoped that it would just all somehow get better."

"So, what is the truth in all this?"

"The truth is that I really don't know what is going on, and I have allowed myself to be victimized by all this change. At this point, I don't have a ton of respect for Donald, but I don't really know him, either. I am waiting for him to come to me, but I could go to him. I could be more proactive."

"Okay, good," said Elizabeth. "What might you like to try that you have not tried yet?"

"I can tell you now that I am going to request a meeting with Donald and ask him some direct questions. And I need to talk to my team. I have not done one-on-one meetings with them in months. That is not good. If I am suffering, they must be, too. And I probably need to spend some time with my mom and process the loss of my dad a bit." Mike let out a big sigh.

Elizabeth was nodding her head fervently. "Yes, yes. Really good work, Mike. Now you know how to 'Go to the Ugly.' I don't want you to expect any 'sky-opening' results. The impact of this exercise is usually felt over time. You may notice small, barely perceptible shifts in your thinking. That is the good stuff we are looking for."

"Actually, I feel a little better already," sighed Mike. "I mean, other than the fact that you have enough evidence on me to end my career," he laughed nervously. "But I do feel a little bit better."

Elizabeth gathered her things and said, "I am glad you feel better. On our way out today, we will shred this list so you don't have to worry about the 'evidence.' Also, I will send you a link to an e-book called *Stress Less for Better Success*. The e-book has the 'Going to the Ugly' exercise in case other resentments from the past surface for you to process the way we did today. Don't be surprised some more issues come up for you. You did a great job today. Thank you for trusting me."

"Thank you, and wow," said Mike. "I guess I do have some baggage."

CHAPTER 16

WEEKEND WARRIOR

Mike got in his car after the session with Elizabeth and noticed a strange and powerful urge within him. He had not felt anything like this since before he and Sonja had children. At first, he could not identify the unusual sensation, but then it hit him. He texted Sonja and let her know he was spending the day at home and then group-texted his team and let them know he would see them on Monday. He could hardly believe what he was about to do.

Mike wanted—no, needed—to clean out his garage. Their home had a two-and-a-half-car garage, yet they could barely fit Sonja's car into it. Mike had been parking in the driveway for more than five years now. Mike was so ashamed and overwhelmed at the thought of the garage that he simply stopped going in there, except to drop off more junk or items that needed to be stored with the promise to himself that he would deal with it later. Later had arrived.

Mike got home and changed into shorts and a t-shirt, grabbed his wireless speaker, opened his ESPN app, and headed to the garage. He started separating things into categories on the driveway. Anyone who drove by might think Mike looked rather violent and angry, but he was actually invigorated. He realized that he had not done anything in the physical labor category other than carrying his daughters and their stuff—like a good Sherpa—in many years, and it felt great.

Around 2:30, Mike realized he hadn't eaten lunch. He jumped in his car and drove to the nearby Home Depot to buy some more clear plastic bins and grab a couple of hot dogs, a bag of chips, and a cold Pepsi.

When Sonja pulled up with the girls at 5:30, Mike was sweeping a very clean two-and-a-half-car garage. Sonja's eyes widened as she took in the organized bins, sports equipment hung in place, and the tidy workbench and landscaping equipment. Mike felt physically fatigued, but also very calm and kind of peaceful—two more sensations he had not felt in years.

Later that night, Mike woke with a start. He felt very alert, considering it was 4:00 a.m. He had another strange idea brewing. He made himself a cup of coffee and left a note for Sonja, letting her know he was going to the office and that he would be back to take his family to breakfast at their favorite place before 10:00 a.m.

Mike felt strange being in his office at 4:30. Early in his career, he had pulled all-nighters working a program or dealing with some computer virus, but he had never arrived at work this early. His office felt almost foreign to him like it was something he had detached from in recent weeks. But all of those piles and files were definitely his—detached or not—so he dug in.

Mike approached his office with the same zeal as he had his garage the day before, but in this case, he cleared every surface and stacked all the files on an extra chair. Then he cleaned all the surfaces, threw away some clutter and junk, and rearranged his books and awards. Now, the entire office was clean except for the giant pile of files and papers in the chair. He sat down with his laptop open and started going through the pile. Many of the papers got shredded since they were financials and memos from the past. For the ones that were part of some current task or project, they were filed and then listed on an Excel spreadsheet (a trick that Albert had taught him for tracking to-dos all in one place) with a tab named for each project. Four cups of coffee and four hours later, his office was clear, his inbox was at zero, and his to-do list was brimming with items.

Mike realized that he felt a strange sense of control over his work, even though he had not completed one task on the list. It felt ridiculously good to get stuff organized. But he had one more thing to do before he headed back home. Mike emailed his boss, Donald Schiffman, and asked for a meeting.

CHAPTER 17

SHOCKER

Mike checked his email on Sunday and was surprised to see that not only had Donald responded, but he suggested they meet for a drink instead of a daytime meeting. The invite was on Monday at 5:00 p.m. Mike had a flash of concern wondering if he was possibly getting fired, and then he chuckled to himself when he remembered that Derek, the new HR guy, would never allow a firing over drinks. He let Sonja know he would be home late on Monday and then attacked the girls' toy pile. He was on a roll with this cleaning and organizing compulsion, and he figured he might as well keep going. He was embarrassed he had let so many things go unattended for so long.

Monday flew by, and Mike left the office to meet Donald over at The Wave, a popular sushi and sports bar nearby. Donald waved to him when he arrived, and as Mike crossed the restaurant to meet him, he felt slightly relieved to see that Derek from HR was not at the table.

The two men shook hands, and Mike ordered a beer. Donald was drinking a martini. Mike felt a little awkward, realizing that he knew absolutely nothing about Donald. Mike thought Donald would have a coffee or milk or something bland to drink. Donald sensed the awkwardness.

"I thought it was time we got to know each other a little bit. I have been through this acquisition thing quite a few times, and I have learned that people need time to get through the shock of change. I am guessing you were especially impacted because Albert was your guy, and then the whole foundation thing was probably not pleasant for you. Seems like it all happened at a not-so-good time in your life, so I felt I should just keep my distance and let you get your feet back under yourself."

Mike appreciated his candor.

"The Bonzo acquisition was actually my fifth in the past eleven years," said Donald. Mike's jaw dropped. "My claim to fame is operational efficiency. I made a deal with MorTech that I would do whatever they wanted for ten years, then I would get my payout and move into consulting. One of the things you learn really fast in M&A[1] is that people almost always flip out over change. There is no avoiding it, and there is no way to control it. I've made so many mistakes early on by trying to be friends with the people whose lives I was changing. I've tried giving them a heads-up on decisions and internal changes, I've tried letting them vent at me and attempting to console them, and I've even tried the firm parental approach but

---

[1] *mergers and acquisitions

all that backfired—occasionally resulting in a lawsuit," he said seriously.

"No matter how much we reassure people," Donald continued, "they still see the change as some sort of a threat. And they also quickly forget what was not working at their former company. In one of our acquisitions, the CEO of the company was well known for verbally abusing nearly everyone on the executive team. I mean yelling at the top of his lungs and threatening people that he would 'F' them up if they did not hit their numbers. He was volatile and ruled with fear, and hardly anyone dared confront him. We had to pay out six lawsuits when we acquired his company. Yet still, the team despised us and resisted our changes. It is just human nature. Now we pretty much come in and do our thing, and while it may seem cold, it is better to give people a few months to adjust."

Mike was in shock. "But wait," Mike said. "You said you had a ten-year buyout, but it has been eleven years. So, are you leaving?"

"Very astute," Donald said. "My wife and I have a twenty-year-old, profoundly disabled son, Marcus. He's a beautiful boy and is also nonverbal and requires nearly constant supervision. He will never live on his own. During MorTech's aggressive growth phase, we moved for the company three times. Moving with our son was a huge burden on my wife, Susan. Marcus does not do well with change, and Susan eventually had to quit her job as a paralegal to help him adjust to each of our new cities.

"Then, I made my deal with MorTech, and we came back here to Spokane. We decided I would commute during the various acquisitions. The last acquisition was headquartered in Chicago, so I lived away from my family for eighteen months and came home when I could. Not easy on Susan at all. Bonzo took a little longer than we thought, so I am eleven months past my due date, and I have agreed to stay another few months—please keep that between us. I am fifty-five years old, and I am going to take my payout and let my wife take her turn. She's forty-five and has decided to go to law school. I want to support her and Marcus now. I can consult on the side a bit, probably with MorTech, but my main focus now is my family."

Mike was stunned. *How could this guy even function after all that?* he wondered. Mike could not help but imagine the additional stress and strain it would cause in his house and on his marriage if one of the girls was disabled. And what if Sonja had never been able to return to work and Mike traveled all of the time? He felt bad for Donald and his family, and for thinking Donald was a heartless jerk.

Crazytown can be confusing.

CHAPTER 18

MIND THE GAP

"Mike, how are things going since we last met?" Elizabeth asked as soon as they sat down.

"Uh, interesting. Very interesting."

Elizabeth tilted her head in Mike's direction, indicating that he should go on.

"After we did that 'ugly' exercise last time, I ended up taking the day off and cleaning out my garage. And it did not stop there. I woke up at 4:00 a.m. the next day and went to the office and cleared my desk and files, and then came home and got after the toy room we have for the girls. I don't know what got into me. It was like I was possessed."

"That sounds very productive," said Elizabeth. "Let's definitely put that on our list of topics today. What else is going on?"

"During the whole clean-up frenzy, I decided I needed to confront Donald, so I reached out to him to schedule a meeting, and he invited me out for a beer. We met on Monday, and he told me about his home life and how many acquisitions he has endured and his history with MorTech. I was so blown away that I hardly spoke while he told his story or even afterward. He could have told me he was an alien from Mars, and I would have believed that more easily than the fact that he was a fiercely loyal corporate executive and husband and father who had sacrificed so much," finished Mike. He purposely left out the detail of Donald leaving MorTech in two months, in case Elizabeth did not know that part.

"Sounds very enlightening," said Elizabeth.

"So, let's widen the lens a little today. Tell me, if in six months you ran into an old friend and the two of you were catching up, what would it take for you to report that you were thriving in your life and work? What does ideal look like for you? Let's make a list."

"First of all, I would stop waking up in the middle of the night in a cold sweat and dreading my job every morning," said Mike immediately.

"That describes what you *don't* want," interjected Elizabeth. "What does it look like then, when things are ideal?"

"Oh, I would sleep at night, every night."

"Good. What else would be on your list?"

Mike started to enumerate them:

"I would wake up rested and excited to go to work.

"I would be working out regularly and eating clean 80 percent of the time. And drinking only moderately.

"I would be learning, and my brain would be challenged and stimulated. I love problem-solving, and I would be doing that every day.

"I would be earning at least 25 percent more than I am now. I am underpaid.

"I would have stock in whatever company I was working for so that the next merger or acquisition presents a big payout for my hard work.

"I would take actual vacations with my family and have more paid time off.

"I would feel excited about my work, and I would be leading a larger team. Much larger."

Elizabeth looked at him curiously. "Tell me about that, Mike. You would like to lead a larger team?"

"Um, that surprised me as it came out of my mouth, too," said Mike. "But it feels very real. I think I have always wanted to lead more people, but I had convinced myself that Albert was the people guy, and I was the IT guy. But it's not true. I may be different than Albert, but I am getting lots of ideas not only about my team but about operations in general. If I were Donald, I think I would do things differently."

"Okay, good realization," said Elizabeth. "Let's continue. Now I want you to make an imaginary horizontal line in your mind. About five inches across. On the right end of the line, I want you to imagine the number ten, the highest. On the left end of that line, put the number one, for the lowest. The ten represents everything you have listed here."

Elizabeth read Mike's list out loud and then continued.

"So, if all of that is present in your life, for the most part, you would put yourself at ten on that scale. The number one, on the left, represents you being lost and confused and hating your life. So, where are you on that scale right now? How does your current situation line up with what you ultimately want your life to look like?"

Mike thought about it for several minutes.

"I am at five. My life is five. I want to be at ten, but I am sitting at five! What my problem is—"

"Okay, good!" interrupted Elizabeth. "Very good. Now tell me why you are at five and not one? What is going well?"

Mike was surprised by this question. He thought she would ask about why he is not at a ten and how he got off track.

"Ahhh, I guess I am at five because I have a great wife and a loving family." Mike continued to list the positive aspects of his life:

"I have a job.

"I have a team I really like and respect.

"I work in technology, which is a good sector. I could go after more if I wanted it.

"I am running again, and I am eating better already. I am at about 50/50 with clean eating, but that is way better than a few months ago when it was more like 98/2.

"I have weeks of unused time off sitting in my PTO account. I could take a vacation at any time.

"Good, good," Elizabeth said. "What are your thoughts about all that?"

"Well, I guess I did not realize that I do have a few things going well."

"Excellent. Now imagine yourself standing on the five line and looking toward the ten and all that it represents for you. Knowing yourself, what guiding principle will close that gap and get you to a ten?"

"Do you mean what actions I need to take?" asked Mike.

"Good question," said Elizabeth. "We will work on the actions later. But for now, I want you to choose a guiding principle that will stay with you while you close the gap over the coming months. Like an attitude or a value."

"I think it is confidence," said Mike uncomfortably. "I think I lost my confidence along the way."

Elizabeth interjected, "Mike, one of the ways we know we are on the right track is if confidence, for example, is the quality or principle that you have needed to work on, maybe, your entire life. Does that feel true?"

"Yes, it does," said Mike. "Yes, it does! It probably had something to do with having an alcoholic father. You learn to shut up and keep quiet and that you can't trust what is around you. That can't have helped."

"So, 'confidence' is your word. Excellent work," said Elizabeth. "'Confidence' is a word I hear a lot in my work as a mentor. People tend to confuse confidence and clarity. Clarity comes from introspection and self-reflection. You can go within and do some work on yourself, and it will help you to be more clear—like some of the work we are doing. But confidence comes only from doing things that are outside of your comfort zone. In other words, you cannot *think* your way to confidence. You will never wake up with more confidence. You have to *do* things that rebuild that confidence muscle. As we wrap up for today, can you think of a few small ways you can work on your confidence in the next two weeks?"

Mike thought about it for a time and then said, "I am going to hire a personal trainer. I have never had any exercise advice, and I am in my forties now. I am going to find one I like and get some advice."

"Good," said Elizabeth. "What else?"

"If you don't mind my saying, I am going to update my résumé and see what roles are out there for me."

"No, of course I do not mind. Our work here is confidential. So, you have your marching orders. I will be interested in hearing about your progress next time if you choose to do the things you mentioned."

CHAPTER 19

THE CAREER COMPASS

Two weeks flew by for Mike, and he found himself once again in session updating Elizabeth. Mike reported that he had worked out twice with the trainer he hired at the gym. The trainer, Lorne, was a former professional soccer player and marathon runner. He had done a fitness assessment on Mike and concluded that Mike was something fitness experts called "skinny and fat." This meant that Mike did not look fat, yet he did not have adequate muscle mass. Not a big surprise to Mike. Lorne was putting together a dietary and workout plan for Mike. They agreed to train twice a week together in the gym for six months, and that Mike would continue running on the other days with one day off per week. So far, he felt tired and sore, and he was only two sessions in.

"I can see what you mean, though," Mike continued. "How doing stuff out of our comfort zone is a way of building confidence. I feel kind of proud of myself. It is humiliating to have some super-fit geek assess me. But it is what it is, and I feel better doing something about it than just continuing and not doing anything about it. It's weird."

"Taking action that creates that feeling of self-esteem is exactly the ingredient that fuels confidence," said Elizabeth. "Glad to hear it."

"I did attempt to do my résumé, but I got stuck. I was thinking I should apply for some stuff that is a total change from what I am doing now. Like maybe I could do tech sales. But I don't know how to make my résumé say that I would be good at sales."

Elizabeth smiled warmly and said, "Yes, it is kind of hard to start a job search until you really know what you want. Initially, I had an exercise planned for us today called 'My Career Superpower.' But I think we should do that next time. Today, I think we need to talk about your career compass."

"I have a career compass?"

"We are going to use the metaphor of a compass to look at some truths about career change for most professionals. Draw a large circle on this piece of paper," said Elizabeth as she handed Mike a blank piece of paper. "Now draw a cross over the circle, so it looks more like a compass. At the top of the compass or North, write the number 360 for 360 degrees. And at the very bottom, write 180 for 180 degrees or South. Put your current title at the 360 mark. Your role as chief technology officer. Write that at the top."

Elizabeth pointed to where Mike had written the letters 'CTO' and continued, "When you are out there in the market applying for roles, this is the role the market recognizes and will respond to by inviting you to interview or even recruiting you. Let's say that you have a mad passion for finance, but you have been in technology all of your career. Even if people have been telling you for years what a finance genius you are, if it is not a direct and obvious part of your formal experience, the market is not likely to take a chance on you."

"So, does this mean I am stuck being a CTO?"

"Not necessarily. But it is important to understand how the market sees you. Think of it in your own hiring. I bet that you tend to hire people who are currently doing the role you need them to do, right?" Mike nodded. "And that is how it works. With few exceptions, companies don't hire—or even interview—people who don't have the current experience they are looking for. The higher your level is, the more this becomes the case. It's not fair, but it is true. Don't give up hope, though; we will come back to this.

"Now, let's look at the bottom, at the 180 degrees," Elizabeth continued. "If you were to move as far away as you can from what you are doing now, that would be like doing a 180 in your career. That would be like opening the kayak shop you mentioned when we first met, right? Or like going to work at something completely different, like construction or opening a restaurant. You would be as far away from what you are currently doing career-wise as you could be. Do you see that?"

Mike nodded.

"There is nothing wrong with doing a 180. Hollywood movies love a 180. You know, where the burned-out corporate lawyer throws her iPhone in the dumpster and becomes a sports agent or the CPA who quits his job and starts a nonprofit that provides lunch to homeless people. It can be very inspiring to consider, and some people do successfully navigate a 180. The thing that we have to keep in mind is that there are two major costs to doing a 180: time and money. It takes time to learn a new business and a new industry. The average learning curve is three to five years. And then there is the money. If you are starting out in a business or industry you don't know it can also take three to five years to get your income back up to where it belongs. The costs of time and money are no reason not to do it, but it is the reality of a 180."

Mike was unpleasantly surprised, but what Elizabeth said made a lot of sense. He knew nothing about owning a business. He could go a little while without his income, but not three to five years.

"So, let's go back up to your current role at the top here. Draw a diagonal line about fifteen degrees to the right and then fifteen degrees to the left of your current role. So, let's call that whole triangular area your 'pivot zone.' This means that you are not stuck. You simply need to come up with career change ideas that are *adjacent* to what you are doing now, but different enough for you to be interested in them. That way, you will not have to give up much time or money to make a change. I will give you one example, and then you need to come up with some on your own. Deal?"

"Deal!"

"You could teach college," said Elizabeth. "There are a number of classes you could teach in your area of expertise at the college level as an adjunct professor. Universities would jump at your résumé and the fact that you have worked in higher-level roles in tech. If your classes fill and you get great reviews from the students, you could eventually secure a full-time position. It would only be about half of your current salary—but you would also have a pension, and with twenty years of work left, that could be worth a lot."

Mike was amazed. He had never even thought about teaching. He did really did like young people and felt he had a way of connecting. He was intrigued.

"Okay, your turn!" said Elizabeth.

Mike was already deep in thought. He silently wondered to himself what would be *adjacent* to what he was doing now. Elizabeth waited patiently.

"I could consult," Mike said excitedly.

"Yes, you most certainly could," said Elizabeth. "In what areas might you like to consult?" she asked.

"I could easily assess a company's growing IT needs and set up the infrastructure and coordinate with their engineers or developers. Those are all of my favorite things, and I can do them in my sleep."

"Bravo! Excellent. What else? Let's see if you can come up with another one."

Everything else that Mike considered was way out of the zone she had outlined. All of the sports-related things, like the kayak shop or becoming a golf pro, were far outside of the "pivot zone."

Mike finally spoke. "Well, if I am thinking pivot, then I could pivot to doing just one aspect of my job but in a larger setting. I could be the chief security officer for a very large company. They might like that I have been a CTO myself. Also, I could do my role but in a different industry. It doesn't have to be software. I could move over to health care or finance, and that might be interesting to me; I think my experience would still get me in the door."

"Great! Now you have the idea. You are not stuck."

Mike silently agreed. He did not feel as trapped as he thought he was.

"I did want to tell you that there are three exceptions to the so-called rule we are discussing about career change. The first is age. If you are in your twenties, you can pretty much land anywhere on the compass, and people will give you a shot. People likely perceive that applicants in their twenties are not set in their ways and can still be molded. Plus, younger people have a lot less to lose. They are usually not getting paid as much, and are more willing to relocate and so there is a perception of less risk in giving them a shot. I am not saying it right, but that is how it works out there.

"The second exception is for sales professionals. Most hiring managers will make the mental leap from one industry, or type of sales, to another quite easily when they are looking at the résumé of a successful sales professional. Now—"

"Sales is something I was thinking of," interrupted Mike. "I could be part of a tech sales team for another company.

Like what Sal and Melinda do on my team. They travel with the sales reps to help close the sale. I could do that."

Elizabeth tilted her head in a way that Mike came to know as an indication that she was about to be sympathetic.

"Mike, it is not likely you will ever get calls for roles that are several levels below your current status even if you are willing to do it," she said calmly. "Sorry. Companies have a natural aversion to hiring someone with too much experience for a role because most have been burned by someone who left the job after six months due to a better offer. Sometimes people apply for lower-level roles when they are feeling desperate 'out there' in the job market. They are often alarmed when they cannot even get calls for jobs below their paygrade and believe that this is an indicator of their overall marketability. But of course, they are not going to get calls below their paygrade because most hiring managers will not consider an overqualified candidate. It has nothing to do with their marketability. They are just playing at the wrong level."

As Mike had come to expect, this logic made perfect sense.

"Okay, let's talk about the third exception," Elizabeth said with a smile. "Anyone with a solid reputation and a network could have someone in a position of power simply pick them up and place them in another career lane entirely—well outside of their pivot zone. It happens all the time. Let's say that your old boss, Albert, lands as the CEO of a new company and he knows your operational abilities. Even though your résumé does not illustrate your special OPS skills, Albert knows you and trusts you. He can vouch for you to the board or other executives, and in the snap of a finger, you are in another lane."

Mike liked the sound of being lifted to another lane, especially working for Albert again, but then became concerned.

"The problem is I don't have a network other than Albert," Mike said, embarrassed.

"Yes, you do," Elizabeth reassured Mike. "We will talk about that soon, but you probably have more of a network than you think. You did a terrific job today. What was meaningful to you?"

Mike smiled. He was becoming accustomed to recaps at the end of any of his meetings with Elizabeth.

"I learned that I am probably not a good candidate for doing a 180 with my career. I mean, it sounds kind of cool to do something dramatically different, but it is silly to throw away everything I have ever done to become a sportswriter or open a kayak shop."

Elizabeth nodded her head, encouraging Mike to continue.

"At the same time, I did realize that I am not stuck. I can pivot to something I'm interested in, still earn what I am worth, and not take forever with a new learning curve. I can kind of cash in or leverage what I have already done and turn it into something else."

"'Leverage' is a terrific word," interjected Elizabeth. "Anything else?"

"Yes, I learned that I couldn't easily just find some random, lower-level job and check out of life for a while because the chances of being hired are slim."

"Well done," Elizabeth nodded. "You did great work here. Now, what about, instead of updating your résumé, you further explore the whole 'pivot' concept? Maybe add one or two more ideas to your list of options, and also do a little research. Maybe make some calls. Dig in a bit."

"Sounds good," said Mike.

CHAPTER 20

MY CAREER SUPERPOWER

That next week Mike felt slightly better at work; Donald pretty much left him on his own, and the IT team was busy onboarding a large, new client that had signed on last month. Mike had discussed his last session and the compass concept with Sonja, and she raised some very useful questions.

At his next visit, Mike walked into the library conference room and found Elizabeth on the phone and scribbling something on a piece of paper. She handed the note to Mike, which said, "SO sorry—I need five minutes!"

Mike gave her the thumbs up, closed the door, and decided to wander among the bookshelves outside of the conference room to give Elizabeth some space.

Elizabeth found Mike a few minutes later. "I am so sorry about that. There were about fifteen people on that call, and it was some very important stuff I needed to hear. I could not jump off." Mike understood but also wondered what it was all about.

"Okay, so how are you?" Elizabeth asked.

"I'm great," answered Mike. "It is really weird in that nothing materially has changed, but I feel different."

"Different, how?" asked Elizabeth.

"Well, I don't feel trapped. I see that I have options. And I have been sleeping through the night again."

"Good to hear," said Elizabeth. "Tell me more about not feeling trapped."

"When we ran into each other at the airport, that was one of the lowest points in my life. I felt like I was completely trapped. I just wanted to escape. I felt no sense of control over my life in Crazytown, as you called it, and at the same time, I felt like an idiot because I have so much to be thankful for."

"And what do you feel has changed?" pressed Elizabeth.

"I guess *I* changed. I realized that I had a lot of baggage about the merger and my dad, and I blamed Donald, and I wasn't sleeping—and then the whole anxiety attack thing. Geez, I sound like a psycho just saying all of this."

"Keep going," said Elizabeth, ignoring his self-critical comment.

"I felt like I was a victim, especially when the foundation went away. But then, I don't know, something shifted. I get it now. I do have choices. Plus, I am running again and working with a trainer, and the house and garage and my office are organized. I feel like I have some control over my life."

"Mike, I am very impressed with the work you have done and with your willingness to self-evaluate and make some changes. This is why I do this mentoring. Work is a very large and important aspect of our lives. When things happen that are painful and even traumatic, our culture tells us to just bite the bullet. But with some effort and self-reflection, most of us can regain a sense of agency in our career and life and make better decisions. Can you imagine the quality of decisions you would have made if you had simply gone home after your anxiety attack, not told Sonja, and not dealt with any of that?"

"I would have probably quit my job the following Monday! Sonja would be confused since she knew nothing about my unhappiness, and I probably would have wandered the neighborhood drinking beers all day."

"That does not sound good," Elizabeth laughed. "Okay, so any insights on the career compass?"

"Yes, I have decided that I do not want to teach school or start a consulting company!"

Elizabeth was surprised by Mike's certainty. "Okay, good. Tell me why."

"I was talking to Sonja about the compass exercise we did, and I talked about the things that were adjacent to what I am doing now. Sonja's company hires a lot of consultants, and she had some good questions. She asked if I liked working alone. And if I would be okay not having a team, per se. Initially, this sounded great because I would not have to deal with all of the aggravation of meetings and the people stuff and payroll and other departments, and so on. But being solo and working from home or in some coworking space is not me at all.

"I don't want to work alone. I feel I am best when I am part of something. And I really like the people stuff when I think about it. Even though I have work to do on the leadership side, I get a lot of good feelings from being an integral part of something.

"Teaching feels like that same thing, only a lot less money. It would take me years to feel connected to the other faculty, so I would be kind of solo and not part of a team. It would be cool to work with so many young people, but too lonely for me."

"There you go!" Elizabeth nodded. "Those sound like some powerful insights. And Sonja asked you some good coaching questions. And yes, for those who succeed as consultants, or even kayak shop owners, there is a huge internal drive to be free of the constraints of a typical job. People who start their own companies often crave independence and an outlet for their strong entrepreneurial longings and feel restricted by their corporate roles. They also have a higher risk tolerance than most. A willingness to risk income, reputation, stability—all of the things that are built into an employment setting. So, where do you go from here?"

"I am making a list of industries that are appealing to me and the few roles I can apply for within my pivot zone, and then I am going to update my résumé and start a quiet search."

"Then what I have planned for today's session will fit right in," said Elizabeth. "One of the most unhelpful things that happened after I got fired was that people kept asking me what I was 'passionate' about." Elizabeth put "passionate" in air quotes. "The passion question made me confused and unsettled. I mean, I like to cook gourmet food, so that was something, but what did that have to do with my formerly illustrious career in finance? I really struggled, but then I had a realization. Would you like to hear what that was?"

Mike nodded.

"The whole concept of monetizing your passion is not helpful when we are in a career crisis. And probably not that helpful at the beginning of a career, either. Some people talk about passion because it comes from our cultural belief that if we do what we love, it will not feel like work. What does that even mean? I am not suggesting that we should do work we hate and ignore our passions. But the whole 'passion' line of thinking is kind of set up for not doing the real work of dealing with baggage and learning to handle the stress and complexities of our careers. Passion is an important part of life, and areas of passion where we lose ourselves in activity are connected to happiness. Absolutely. But that does not mean that it will be a good choice for our primary work."

"That actually makes a lot of sense," said Mike. "I mean, maybe I just need to go kayaking a few times a month or go on a solo kayak trip for a few days a year. But opening a kayak shop could be a mistake for me. What do I really know about owning a shop? Also, I think I would hate scheduling people for shifts and dealing with vendors and all that. None of it sounds good except for the kayaking part."

Elizabeth smiled. "I am glad you found that useful. What I have discovered is that instead of figuring out our passion, it is more productive to discover our career superpower; some gifts or ways of working that we bring to whatever we do regardless of our title or role.

"Mike, for this exercise, I want you to imagine yourself in line with one hundred other CTOs from around the globe," Elizabeth gestured to the back of the room. "Picture all kinds of industries and all kinds of companies, but all CTOs crowded right here in this room. Now put yourself in that group, too. Tell me, for what reason or skill do you easily and effortlessly pop to the front of that line?"

"As a CTO?" asked Mike.

"Yes."

"Customer-centric project management."

"Okay, good," said Elizabeth. "What does customer-centric project management look like when you do it?

"Most CTOs focus on the process and the engineering, and they try to make the customer comply and adjust to the tech, but I think that approach is backward. This is not just some software that is the stand-alone crown jewel of an organization. The technology has to integrate and be as user-friendly as possible for the customer, or it is an abject failure."

"Good. Give me another reason you pop to the front of the line."

"People skills first."

"Okay, what does 'people skills first' look like when you do it?"

"Most IT departments are allowed to hide behind the myth that to be good, they have to be freakishly antisocial and siloed from the organization. This myth lets that kind of team get away with all kinds of poor communication habits, and that creates division within the company, and often with the customers as well. Albert taught me that everyone needs a certain emotional intelligence level to work in today's culture. Everyone can be held to a basic standard of responsiveness and communicate in a professional manner. The people and relationships come first, then if you want to be an IT genius, great, but the people skills must come first."

"Okay, wow. I like all that. Very good. What else?"

Mike thought about it for a while.

"Other departments matter. This is kind of connected to the other two, but also it stands on its own. Departments like HR, operations, sales, and customer experience matter. I try to attend their meetings, and I invite them to attend portions of ours; knowing what each of those departments is dealing with is critical to how we do our work."

"Excellent! Now I want you to picture that group again and tell me a problem you love to solve that everyone else in that line will bristle at. Not that you love problems, but what problem do you excel at solving?"

"When the customer has a complexity specific to their company, and no one has been able to solve it in the past. Figuring it out is the cause of great stress, but I really like gathering the team and focusing intensely on that problem. It's like that scene in *Apollo 13*, where all of the engineers have to figure out how to get Tom Hanks and his team home from space using only the materials they have on the spacecraft. I thrive in that environment."

"Now tell me, growing up, what was your unspoken role in your family?"

Mike was surprised that they were talking about his childhood, but the answer came easily. "Peacemaker."

"Okay, good. One last question, and then we will have your career superpower. What is your secret weapon? Everyone has one. It is usually something you use all the time but maybe something you would not advertise. What might that be for you?"

Mike was thinking deeply, and then the answer came to him. "My secret weapon is my ability to listen. People tell me stuff. Like Donald, a few weeks back. I hardly said a word, and he told me his whole life story. Maybe more than he intended. It's always been like that for me. I am a good listener."

"Excellent. So, let's take stock of your entire career superpower. These are things that you bring to the table no matter what you do for a living. To recap, the list is:

- Customer-centric project management

- People skills first

- Other departments matter

- Solving complex customer problems

- Being a peacemaker

- Being a good listener

"Those are your superpowers. That entire list. I tricked you a little bit because some of that exercise was interview rehearsal."

Mike raised one eyebrow at Elizabeth.

"Hey, I do not want you to leave MorTech. But you have said you want to explore and I want to help you prepare. Forget all of the silly interview questions and answers online career blogs offer. You need to be able to talk easily about what separates you from others. And by the way, you light up when you talk about those things."

Mike shifted as he thought back to his recent internet searches on the topic of interviewing as Elizabeth continued.

"My suggestion is that you come back later with real-life examples and stories of how you used those superpowers in your role, and if you can add some data or results, you will crush any interviews you have."

Mike was stunned and grateful.

"But for our work here," Elizabeth said, "I want you to chart your roles and your time at Bonzo and MorTech on a scale of one through ten. A ten is when you got to use all of your superpowers at work. What was going on, and why did you give that phase a high score? Then your low points. What was happening? Come back next time with some insights about your work over the years against the backdrop of using or not using your superpowers."

"Got it," said Mike as he rose to leave.

"But wait! What was useful today?"

"Wow, everything was useful. I feel a lot more confident going into interviews now that I have these talking points. And some of them I did not even really realize—like the problem I love to solve. It makes so much sense, and yet I have never thought about it. I have never thought about any of this. I mean, people should know this about themselves. I am going to go home and ask Sonja these questions. I will ask my team, as well. And also, the passion stuff was helpful. I was going to get on the wrong track with that passion thinking. It reminded me that I need more passion in my life, but that does not mean I need to make it into a business."

"Very good to hear. Uncovering the problems we love to solve can enlighten us on what work we can do tirelessly. On the contrary, if our work consists of problems we hate solving, that is not a recipe for longevity.

"And you should know that, occasionally, people do start a business, and monetize their passion and it works out beautifully. But they are few and far between. Plus, if you peel back the layers, their success often has more to do with their superpower than their passion, but you get the idea."

And with that, they shut off the room lights and left. Elizabeth's mind instantly shifted back to the shocking conference call she'd been on before today's meeting with Mike. Significant changes were afoot at MorTech.

CHAPTER 21

BLIND SPOTS

When Mike arrived at the conference room, Elizabeth was already sitting at the table. She broadly smiled when he came into the room.

"Mike, do you recall when we first met, I explained that anyone in a career crisis needed to work through four major buckets? The first and perhaps the most important bucket is to deal with stress like a boss. That is the powerful work that most of us never do because our culture tells us to endure negativity and not dwell on the past. Not dealing with our stress causes us to make bad career decisions. But you have bravely wrestled your work 'demons,' figured out what you really want, explored your career superpower, which was part of the second bucket, and discovered how important building confidence is to your overall plan. This also means that we are almost done with our work together."

"Really? I don't feel almost done."

"Well, you are. You have done the big work of self-examination. You are more aware, and you know how to channel your anger and frustration—just ask your garage and office. Also, you are taking better care of yourself. No anxiety attacks, right? You are sleeping through the night and are more compassionate toward yourself and others. You have made some giant leaps in building that confidence muscle. We could stop here, and you would be in good shape for making excellent career decisions. But we do have a couple more things to look at. The last two buckets are not quite as psychological as the first two, so we will move through them more quickly, but they are just as important. The next steps are about finding your blind spots and then activating your network for career leverage. How does that sound?"

"Um, good?" answered Mike reluctantly, chuckling. "Do I have blind spots?"

"We all do," assured Elizabeth. "If you were on my team, I would strongly encourage you to do a 360 evaluation. This is where you get objective, anonymous feedback from your team, peers, and boss. If done right, it can be a powerful experience. But since you do not work for me, we will have to rely on your own self-evaluation, which can also be useful.

"I would like to ask you about your communication habits under the umbrella of emotional intelligence. Emotional intelligence is, at its core, how we deal with the outside strain that life pushes upon us, as well as awareness of our emotions and the emotions of others."

Elizabeth placed a diagram in front of Mike. It had a long horizontal line. On the far left of the line, it had the words "passive-aggressive." On the far right, it had the words "aggressive-aggressive." Mike was intrigued.

"Let's think about our approach to conflict or the external stress we were talking about. So, on the right here is aggressive-aggressive. When pushed, some people default here. They consider communication to be a battle, and they see others as adversaries. They are blunt, even brutal, in their directness and see conversations as win/lose—and they don't like losing. They interrupt people or talk over them; they are not great listeners, and they are often intimidating and not very collaborative. Aggressive communicators are often baffled when others feel hurt by their words or attacked by them. Have you ever known anyone like this?"

"Uh, yeah, that would be my dad when he was drunk."

"Okay, sorry to hear that. Now on the other extreme, is passive-aggressive. Notice I did not say passive-passive. There is no such thing as someone who is completely passive. Passive people show their dissatisfaction aggressively, but in a passive way—like rolling their eyes on the lighter side of being passive to completely shutting down on the more serious side. This person is more likely to hint rather than be direct, but often, their hints are so indirect they go unnoticed. People who default to passive-aggressiveness under stress will let important, even critical conversations go unaddressed, or they wait so long that the conversation becomes pointless. They can be a little sarcastic or snarky because they are not dealing with their true feelings, so the feelings can come out a bit sideways. But usually, they fool no one. Do you know anyone like this?"

"That would be me," laughed Mike.

"We all have a default setting in one extreme or the other. The default setting is a blind spot for about 90 percent of us. Mine is in the aggressive-aggressive zone. In my twenties, I was very combative. I had some very loud confrontations with some of the guys I worked with on Wall Street and even a couple of bosses along the way. I still get embarrassed when I think of it.

"But there is a middle ground that all of us need to work toward. From an emotional intelligence perspective, that middle ground is called *assertiveness*. Assertiveness is learning how to find our voice and say what needs to be said without being passive or aggressive. Assertiveness is standing our ground or delivering tough news in a clear way that people can hear, and not letting important conversations go unaddressed. Assertiveness is a learned behavior. It takes practice and thought. None of us are born knowing how to do this stuff—we must work at it. For example, because I tend toward the aggressive, I had to work at becoming a better listener and not always being the first to talk. I worked on being more thoughtful about my responses, especially when I was stressed, and still, to this day, I have to remind myself to be assertive instead of aggressive in board meetings and other settings where I have strong opinions.

"So, let's go back to a very stressful time for you, like when Albert was let go. If you slow down time and look back at that, what was your response?" asked Elizabeth.

"I completely shut down," said Mike. "I felt like it was all happening *to me*, and I shut down."

"If you could rewind that whole situation, what might you do differently?"

Mike's expression furrowed. "I see now that I was completely passive. I should have done more to connect with my team even though I did not have answers. I thought if I said anything at all, that I would just lose my temper. But saying and doing nothing was a mistake. Donald was working on-site for a week before he emailed me. I am an executive of the company, I could have just stopped by his office and introduced myself, but I was being proud and passive, and waited for him to come to me. By the time I got that email to review my department, I was seething.

"The same goes for the CEO. I am embarrassed now that I think of it," Mike admitted. "I could have just asked his admin to put me on his schedule. Then I could have asked my questions. But I somehow convinced myself that it would be too aggressive of a move. I don't know what the outcome would have been, but now I see that it was just passive-aggressiveness."

Elizabeth listened intently and took notes as Mike continued.

"Albert was such a good mentor and taught me to have one-on-one meetings with the team. On some level, I guess I thought they were a pain in the butt, so I just did it to tick the box. I was just wasting everyone's time. So, what kind of leader am I really? I thought Donald was a jerk when maybe I am the jerk for neglecting my team. I mean how could I not know this stuff about—"

Elizabeth interjected. "Not helpful! Insulting yourself is not helpful. Let's interrupt that pattern. Maybe you were doing the right thing, Mike. It seems like you have good retention of your team. Do you think it's too late? Has too much damage been done?"

"No, it's not too late," said Mike.

"So, then what is the blind spot lesson as it relates to your team and leadership?"

"I feel like I get it now. All that stuff the experts talk about as it relates to trust and connection, I get it. My job is not to just run the team and leave them alone to nail our projects. I mean, it is that, of course, but it is also to create an environment where there is some connection and meaning to the goals and the vision. My job is to make them feel supported and help them develop in their careers and to care about their lives. Basically, everything I have faulted the new leadership for not doing with me."

"If we refer to it as an evolution of your leadership, then how do you move forward?"

"Look," said Mike, "I still have my doubts about MorTech and my place there. But while I am there, I am going to change my focus. I mean, I am not going to get all touchy-feely with everyone, but I will get us together more to work on vision and planning, and I will ask about how their lives are going as well. I got so much of my own sense of meaning out of the foundation project, and yet I also have a whole team of people who have complicated lives, just like I do, and I want to pay more attention to that."

"Excellent," said Elizabeth. She was thrilled with Mike's progress and had a secret idea germinating in her mind.

CHAPTER 22

WHO KNEW?

When Mike got back to his office that morning, he sent an email to each of his direct reports and asked them to put a one-on-one meeting on their calendars within the next two weeks, and to come ready to discuss their current projects, what support they needed, and any thoughts they had about their career development. It felt like it had been an eternity since he was emotionally present for his team. He felt even worse about it when the invites came streaming in within minutes of his email. *They must be hungry for some contact.* He had some making-up to do with his team.

Over the next two weeks, Mike had one-on-one conversations with all eight direct reports. He focused on listening and asking good questions and broke his habit of asking a status update question followed by, "and do you need anything from me?" In retrospect, Mike realized that this question was really code for "Okay, get out so I can get back to work." Instead, he gently asked about their home lives.

Mike learned a lot about his team. He had no idea, for example, that Lisa was married to a woman named Ricky. He had always assumed Ricky was a guy. Lisa had worked for Mike for four years. How was it possible he knew nothing personal about Lisa after four years? Also, he had no idea that Neal, who was only twenty-nine years old, owned two houses, one apartment building, and was planning to buy another rental house within the month. Mike was impressed and surprised at how ambitious Neal seemed. The list of surprises about his team went on for two weeks.

Mike was starting to see what Elizabeth meant about building confidence by doing stuff outside of his comfort zone. He felt surprisingly good and better about himself overall.

CHAPTER 23

WHAT NETWORK?

Elizabeth was thrilled to hear about Mike's progress with his team.

"So, are we going to find more blind spots?" asked Mike as they sat down.

"For most of us, our blind spot is a singular thing that wreaks havoc in a lot of places in our lives. Would you say that your passivity meets that description? Has it impacted other areas of your life?"

"Well, yeah, I think it has been a pretty big deal for me— for as long as I can remember. After our last session, I was having flashbacks of the many times I have let things go unsaid both personally and professionally. It is not good when you have strong feelings about stuff but never say it. It's not like I love conflict now, but I am committed to addressing things quickly and asking more direct questions. I had a one-on-one with each of my direct reports. I have a long way to go, but I can tell already that the mojo in my department has changed. All from one meaningful conversation."

Mike was slightly alarmed to see that Elizabeth's eyes were filled with tears.

"Excuse me," said Elizabeth when she realized Mike had stopped talking. "I am moved by what you are saying. I hope I am not embarrassing you. I am so impressed that you have grown so much in such a short time. The whole Crazytown thing can cause so much pain and suffering in our lives. A shift in perspective like yours is a game-changer. It takes a person from feeling victimized to feeling a sense of agency and empowerment. That is why I do this mentoring work."

"It was you and all the time you spent with me," said Mike.

"No, Mike, it was not me. I gave you some space and asked you some questions, but you did all the work. You came to the conclusions, not me. The human brain is a marvel. Once those new, positive neural pathways are created, the good stuff just builds and builds."

Mike smiled.

"Okay," Elizabeth said, composing herself and opening her laptop. "It is time to talk about the last bucket: your network and how to leverage it so that you feel less victimized by change, and by Crazytown, in the future. We are probably going to come up with quite a to-do list today, so I suggest we skip our next meeting and talk again in a month. That way, you will have time to tackle that list. Let's take a look at your LinkedIn profile," Elizabeth said as she typed.

"Oh, that is going to be embarrassing. I haven't updated it in years. I don't even know what it looks like."

"That is not uncommon. People get busy. They have their heads down and are focused on the tyranny of the urgent. But our careers are an entity in and of themselves. Your career can and should be a vehicle for you. But you have to put some effort into it outside of the work that happens every day."

Elizabeth stared at the computer for a minute and then turned it around for Mike to see. "Yes, I would say this needs a couple of hours of work—all fixable stuff. I have a list of suggestions that I compiled for one of my classes," Elizabeth said, placing a list of LinkedIn suggestions in front of him. "You will see that at the top of this list is a professional headshot. Is this a selfie you've got here?"

"Yep," replied Mike.

"Enough said," smiled Elizabeth as she slid the LinkedIn tip sheet closer to him and closed her laptop. "What about your network? When was the last time you reached out to your college alumni association? Are you part of that network?"

"Oh man, not since my first year out of undergrad, and I am embarrassed to say I've never attended one event at the university where I received my master's. I figured they would only try to collect donations from me."

"Okay, so this is an easy one: Get on their mailings lists, check out the websites, and make a note of any career services they offer like résumé writing, for example. You paid all of that tuition, and there might be a number of services you find interesting or useful. And find out if they have any local events scheduled. Some of the schools offer professional development workshops, industry-specific panels, and social events. It might prove to be useful at this juncture."

Mike was writing quickly.

"I am going to assume that you have not stayed connected with former coworkers over the years. Do you think you could come up with a list of twenty people to connect with on LinkedIn?"

"Yes, I can come up with twenty names."

"For now, you are just going to connect. Later, you might reach out to them and find out what they are up to career-wise. You are not asking for anything. Just connecting. Make sense?"

Mike hesitated before replying, "That's not really me. I mean, reaching out to people. I would not know what to say after all this time."

"It is something outside of your comfort zone certainly, but that makes it kind of good for you, yes?"

"I guess."

Sensing Mike's hesitation, Elizabeth said, "Imagine for a minute that you had been fired along with Albert that day. Other than Albert, who would you have had in your network that could've helped you land elsewhere so that you could take care of your family?"

"Uh, no one," Mike answered sheepishly.

"I am not suggesting that you reach out to people you have not seen in ten years and become best friends or ask them for job leads. That would be contrary to building a network. I am asking you to consider that you do have some professional history with these people and that you can simply reach out and see if they want to catch-up sometime. A phone call, maybe a beer if it is someone you really like. Maybe they need something from you, and you can be useful to them. Helping others can go a long way to building a network. The goal here is a bit of visibility, but you get to do that in a way that feels authentic to you.

"Next is to research what communities, associations, or conferences are related to your industry."

"I already know what they are. Albert made me research them, and I have a list. He wanted me to attend at least one major conference and two local events per year."

"Albert sounds like a great leader, Mike. I get why you were so impacted when he left."

"Yeah, he was. The thing is, I never did attend the conference or any events. I meant to, I just never got around to it."

"Tell me, Mike, why do you think Albert wanted you to attend those conferences and events? Was it because he thought you didn't know how to do your job?"

"That's funny because it is what I thought when he brought it up. He said it was because he wanted me to meet people that shared my interests and to stay excited about innovation."

"Brilliant! And what is the point, do you think of meeting like-minded people and staying excited about innovation?"

"I think I would not mind networking, or whatever, with people in my industry rather than just meeting random people. And I am very interested in innovation. I just have not made the time."

"Okay, good stuff. Now tell me what is slightly outside of your current expertise that is of interest to you? Something that is off in the future somewhere?"

"Oh! Robotics and artificial intelligence," Mike answered quickly.

"Good, while you are at it, how about if you research what conferences or groups are happening in that space?"

"Why?" asked Mike.

"A couple of reasons, actually. First and foremost, our brains need novelty. Our brains are creative, problem-solving machines. But to get our best work, we need to provide a little novelty. Something different or unusual or that challenges our understanding really activates the brain.

"The other reason is that it keeps you connected to the future. AI and robotics, for example, are going to be part of all of our futures. It can give you leverage to know things before the general public does. Specific knowledge is a key type of leverage that most of us don't even realize we have. Make sense?"

"Yep," said Mike.

"So what is on your to-do list?"

Mike referenced his notes. "I am going to update my LinkedIn profile and my résumé while I am at it. I'll connect with at least twenty people and maybe reach out to a few to see what is up with them.

"I'll reach out to both of my alumni organizations and find out what their career services departments have to offer.

"I'll find out what conferences are coming up and what events are available and what I might attend.

"And I'll do some research on AI and robotics and figure out how I can learn more about that. Wow, that is quite a list. I am glad we will not be meeting for a month."

"And what was helpful today?" Elizabeth asked.

"I am never going to neglect my network again. It really is less complicated than I thought. I don't have to go to random networking events and talk to people about nothing. I can go to conferences and events where the people are like me. I might help a few people from my network because they could be going through something worse than what I was going through. And I can stay connected to my interests and call it networking at the same time. I might even take some of my team with me."

"Nice work," said Elizabeth. "And if I may add: If you were in full-on job search mode, you would cultivate some of those contacts and learning opportunities carefully into informational interviews where you ask people to tell you about their role or company. Then, over time you help those people understand what you are looking for and ask for relevant introductions. Believe it or not, that is how I ultimately ended up at MorTech. I had lunch with a distant contact who made a few introductions, and one of them happened to be head of treasury for our private equity firm. The rest is history."

Mike was about to agree when Elizabeth interjected.

"Oh, and it will actually be six weeks before we speak again. I am taking my kids and their significant others to Hawaii for nine days. I have some big projects coming up, and I want to be fully rested and ready to go when I get back. See you then, okay?"

"Sounds good," said Mike.

CHAPTER 24

CHANGE IS AFOOT

Mike could not believe how much had transpired over the last six weeks. Not only had he followed through with all of the items on his "Elizabeth" list, but he also met with the career advisor at his former university, took some interesting assessments, and got some helpful advice on his résumé.

He also accidentally got a job offer.

One of the calls he'd made during his outreach on LinkedIn was to his old buddy, Craig. Craig was his friend who'd encouraged Mike to keep an open mind when MorTech took over and Albert was fired. Craig had received a large payout when his last employer sold the company, and now he was starting up his own software shop. Craig and the engineers had all of the R&D finished and had major funding lined up. Craig had offered Mike the role of CTO. In exchange for half of his normal salary, Mike would get significant equity in the company right from the start. He would be an investor and would be involved in key decisions about the product, customers, and the team. Craig explained the investors were experts in getting technology to market with the goal of selling the company in three years. If everything went well, Mike would stand to make a lot of money—more money than he had ever imagined.

Mike was intrigued, and a little bit terrified. What Craig was proposing was both exciting and risky. He thanked Craig and told him he needed to think about it and talk to Sonja.

He was pondering all of this when Elizabeth came in for their mentoring session. After they talked about Hawaii and Mike gave his update, he told her about his job offer with Craig and the startup.

"Mike, I must tell you I am not the least bit surprised. You have a lot to offer, and anyone who knows you would get that. I mean, wow, that's two job offers in one week."

"Two? I only have one offer, not two."

Elizabeth smiled broadly and said nothing for what seemed like a long time. "Mike, do you recall that day I asked you to leave the room because I was finishing up an important call? Well, that was an emergency board meeting for MorTech, where I was asked to take over as CEO of the company."

Mike's eyes looked like saucers.

"After careful consideration, I have decided to take it. John, the current CEO, will now run a separate division under our parent company for all future acquisitions. And as I suspect you may already know, Donald is leaving to finally spend time with his family. My vision for MorTech is much more aligned with the culture that you and Albert created at Bonzo, and my focus will be software, not acquisitions. I am putting together an offer for you to be our new COO."

Mike felt a charge of electricity go through him as she said, "COO." He was searching for some words to respond to Elizabeth, but nothing came out.

"I want you to know that I had absolutely no idea this was even a consideration for either of us while I was working with you—that is, until that day when the board called a meeting. I would not want you to think I had any ulterior motives in our work together. On the contrary, by complete accident, I discovered what a quality person you are and what a great leader you can be with the right culture. Your ability to self-reflect and your willingness to learn and change is remarkable, not to mention your career superpowers such as people first and other departments matter.

"As I said, I need to put together an offer, but what I can tell you right off is that together you and I would be setting the culture of this organization. By now, you know I value a learning environment, open dialogue, and of course, results—not too different from what you were used to at Bonzo—but on a much bigger scale. And I would greatly value and need your perspective on the direction of the business and would be counting on your ability to lead and retain top talent."

Mike still sat, speechless and stunned.

"I will also say this," Elizabeth continued, "I am very competitive, and I do not like losing. Your friend, Craig, is not going to get you that easily. Keep an eye on your email tonight for an offer I expect will make you think twice about going to work for some risky startup," she smiled. "And I don't negotiate. I will send you the very best offer I can put together, and it's a take-it-or-leave-it proposition. If you decide to go the other direction, no harm, no foul. I will accept my loss and move on."

Finally, Mike was able to speak. "What's your timing on this, Elizabeth?"

"The announcement is Tuesday. I would like to know your answer by Monday."

Mike swallowed hard then congratulated Elizabeth on her new role as CEO. He shook her hand and told her how grateful he was for the offer, and for the time she invested in him over the last few months. It occurred to him that, either way, his mentoring with her was over. It had been a remarkable experience for him. He felt a little choked up.

Mike sat in his car for quite some time. He knew he could never again have life as it was when Albert was there because that was in the past. He was finally done resisting that reality. Mike thought about the whole concept of Crazytown and how, on the one hand, it's caused by what is happening around us—or to us. Albert did get fired, and his departure was handled callously. Don was cool and kept his distance during the initial stages of the merger. Mike was indeed forced to make cuts on his team and his beloved foundation. Those things happened.

On the other hand, Mike thought about how Crazytown is also how we perceive what is happening around us. Mike realized that he had stopped living up to his leadership potential years ago, and that he had been complacent in his working relationship with Albert. Mike realized that if all of those things happened again, he would be so much more self-aware and self-confident, and he'd respond differently. He was amazed that he was even having such a thought.

He recalled meeting Elizabeth at O'Hare when she said that his career crisis could end up being a gift. He had thought she was nuts at the time, but here he was, some months later feeling entirely grateful for all of it.

Normally Mike did not immediately know how he felt about things. He usually pondered decisions, doubted himself, and then the pondering would turn into analysis paralysis. The bigger the decision, the more agonizing the process. But that was not the case today. Mike had a sense of clarity he had not felt since falling in love with Sonja.

Mike wanted that COO job.

Sonja picked up on the first ring. "Let's get a babysitter tonight," said Mike. "We have some big decisions to make!"

APPENDIX

Reader Resources:

For Brenda's other books, including the free e-book, *Stress Less for Better Success*, please visit:
https://managementmomentum.net/books

To subscribe to Brenda's weekly Coaching Minute: Powerful Insights for Professionals, please visit our site and click the subscribe link:
https://managementmomentum.net/

For a variety of free assessments, including the Career Change Readiness Quiz and the Authentic Career Confidence Assessment, please visit:
https://managementmomentum.net/assessments

To learn about purchasing scientifically validated testing for you or your team, please visit:
https://managementmomentum.net/team-developement

*The fictional non-profit in the book, called the Hope Foundation, was inspired by real-life non-profit called Blue Star Recycling. Please visit their site and consider supporting this mighty little organization that helps employ people who otherwise have a barrier to employment. http://bluestarrecyclers.org/

ACKNOWLEDGMENTS

People often compare writing a book to having a baby. Having done both, I would have to agree with the analogy. Both events are more difficult than any of us imagine, even though our friends try to warn us, and intensely rewarding once it's all over. Also, neither can be done without the help of others. I would like to thank the following helpers:

I am grateful to my clients for trusting me and sharing their very own Crazytown stories—however unbelievable they seemed. I am immensely grateful for what I learned at Erikson Coaching College, where I received my initial coaching credential. Elizabeth would not have been a good mentor without the brilliant coaching tenets I learned there.

I would like to thank Beth Smith and Allison Tabor for introducing me to Henry DeVries, the editor of this book. I cannot imagine any busy author doing a book without Henry and his team at Indie Books International. I thank Mark LeBlanc, who is Henry's business partner, and coincidentally my first-ever business coach many years ago.

I thank Bill Morris and Peter Van Genderen for information about the world of recycling electronics and employing adults with disabilities. Also, our friend Greig Veeder for teaching me the Aggressive-Passive model many years ago.

Special thanks to my dearest friends, Dr. Carrie McCrudden, who reviewed the material on brain science as it relates to habits and alcohol dependency and to Mary LoVerde, who toiled over every word of this manuscript with me like it was one of her own. I am eternally grateful.

And finally, gratitude to my husband Kevin Hood, the love of my life and my greatest fan. And to our remarkable son, Noah. You make me proud every day.

ABOUT THE AUTHOR

Brenda Abdilla is a career and leadership coach who works with corporate leaders who want more effective strategies for team accountability and change management. She also works with professionals who are navigating a change in their high-level careers.

More than 90 percent of Brenda's coaching clients get promoted, land the role they desire, or address their core issues within twelve months of engaging with Brenda.

Brenda's corporate clients, such as Xcel Energy, Regal Cinemas, Vail Resorts, SCL Health, and Comcast, also hire her to deliver workshops on critical topics like emotionally intelligent teamwork, how to be a better leader, and her most popular program: Time Rehab. Brenda's custom programs often impact learning on a deeper level with insights gleaned from personality assessments like The Enneagram, Emergenetics, DiSC, Birkman, and The Emotional Intelligence Quotient.

As a result of working with Brenda, her clients and audiences report they come away with much better tools for dealing with today's complexities, understanding their specific blind spots, learning how to activate their professional network, and finding their unique career superpower.

Outsmarting Crazytown is Brenda's second career book. Her first is *What's Your Lane: Career Clarity for Moms Who Want to Work a Little, A lot, or Not at All* (2013).

On a personal note, Brenda is a devoted foodie who loves cooking and feeding people. Her claim to fame is having fed sixty people a gourmet sit-down dinner with no catering help and only one oven.

Brenda can be reached by phone at 303-456-1210 or at https://managementmomentum.net/

Made in the USA
Monee, IL
19 March 2021